D0264973
WITHDRAWN
005 470

UNEXPLAINED MYSTERIES OF THE WORLD

UNEXPLAINED
MYSTERIES
OF THE WORLD
AN ILLUSTRATED SURVEY OF
THE STORIES • THE MYTHS • THE FACTS
JOHN GRANT

NEW
BURLINGTON
BOOKS

A QUINTET BOOK

Published by New Burlington Books
6 Blundell Street
London N7 9BH

ISBN 1-85348-339-7

This book was designed and produced by
Quintet Publishing Limited
6 Blundell Street
London N7 9BH

Creative Director: Peter Bridgewater
Designer: Annie Moss
Project Editors: Caroline Beattie, Judith Simons,
Damian Thompson
Editor: Susan Baker
Picture Researcher: Liz Eddison
Illustrator: Lorraine Harrison

Typeset in Great Britain by
Central Southern Typesetters, Eastbourne
Manufactured in Hong Kong by
Regent Publishing Services Limited
Printed in Hong Kong by
Leefung-Asco Printers Limited

The material in this book previously appeared in
Great Mysteries and *The Great Unsolved Mysteries
of Science*.

CONTENTS

PART 1

PART 2

INTRODUCTION
IS SEEING BELIEVING?

THERE IS AN OLD Chinese curse: 'May you live through interesting times.'

Whether we regard ourselves as cursed or not, there can hardly be any question that the times we live in are interesting. To look on the dark side, wars and human greed conspire to ensure that all too many of us die through violence or through starvation. On the other hand, most readers of this book will remember the magical moment when, for the first time, a human being walked on the surface of the moon. The Soviet Union is planning to send people to Mars before the end of the century. All over the world, genetic engineers claim that their discoveries will soon be able to obviate hereditary mental retardation, crop failures and many other of the evils that beset humanity. Computer scientists – notably in Japan – predict that within the next decade or so they will be able to construct computers as intelligent and creative as human beings.

These are indeed interesting times.

One of the ways in which they are interesting is that our worldview is in a state of flux. For untold centuries our ancestors were eagerly credulous, believing implicitly in each new 'marvel'. Then science came along, and for the past couple of centuries intelligent people believed only in phenomena that could be reproduced in the laboratory – or, in the case of astronomy, observed by all and sundry.

During this century, things have changed. A number of scientists have realized that there are some things which current science is incapable of explaining, that it is no longer possible to dismiss *all* sightings of UFOs or reports of poltergeists as silly-season stories. It is necessary to examine such events, to reveal them as hoaxes or misinterpretations if that is indeed the case, and to investigate the ones left over – the ones that are, in every sense of the word, mysteries.

Part 1 is in two sections. The first is concerned with mysteries that seem certainly connected with the human mind and body; the second deals with 'external' phenomena, such as UFOs and the Yeti. In a way, this differentiation is artificial, because we have no real reason to believe that may if not all of the 'external' phenomena are not likewise products of the human mind.

Before we examine these mysteries, there are a couple of things we must bear in mind. The first is the 'improbability law'. This has been derived empirically, and states the following in the field of mysteries, the more apparently ridiculous a phenomenon is, the more likely it is to be genuine. The corollary is that, if a particular paranormal power or event is, as it were, 'socially acceptable', then we should view it with some suspicion. It is as if the intuition of our intellects (to coin an apparent contradiction in terms) is profoundly unreliable when it comes to examining the paranormal. In a rather different context, Arthur C Clarke came close to this when he produced his famous First Law· 'When a distinguished but elderly scientist states that something is possible, he is almost certainly right. When he states that something is impossible; he is very probably wrong.'

It would seem that our intellects are like a 'distinguished but elderly scientist', dismissing out of hand everything that does not fit in with a strictly rationalist world-view. In many cases, of course, this 'scientist' is quite right, pigs do not fly. But when it comes to the paranormal the 'scientist' makes grave errors of judgment, which possibly give us a clue as to the nature of mysteries. It is our intellect – the 'scientist' inside each one of us – that tells us what is probably and what is not. If other people see a shower of hazelnuts fall inexplicably from the sky, all our intellect can do is look at the hazelnuts; it rejects the testimony of the observers. Yet our intellect is not doing so for any properly scientific reason; it is perfectly possible that the laws of nature are such that every now and then the sky precipitates hazelnuts. We just do not know – and so automatic intellectual rejection of the notion is highly unscientific. There may be a perfectly rationalist explanation of such phenomena, fitting in happily with the ideas of modern science. It may be that the mystery has been born from the imaginations of hoaxers (although it is hard to picture people staggering around with sacks of hazelnuts just to get their pictures in the local newspaper); but equally it may be that there are some things about this world and this universe about which we understand absolutely nothing.

This is not just an unhelpful 'there are more things in heaven and earth' comment. Obviously, there is an infinitude of things which science does not yet know – there have been scientific proofs that we can *never* know everything; yet science has roughed out a very good picture of the way that nature behaves, even if it will be forever incapable of painting in the details. What we are referring to are images that do not even appear in the picture – laws of which we have not even the slightest inkling.

ABOVE: *"Gnome" with Elsie Wright, photographed by Frances Griffiths at Cottingley Glen, West Yorkshire (England), in September 1917.*

It is, perhaps, precisely because we have not the faintest notion of such natural activities that the improbability law' comes into play. A shower of hazelnuts is an affront to our intellects because whatever brought it about is totally outside our current scientific knowledge. If we had even a smidgeon of understanding of what ws going on, then the event would no longer be a mystery; instead, it would be a subject for scientific examination.

It is worth bearing in mind the 'improbability law' as we examine the various mysteries discussed in Part 1. A second factor to remember is the divided brain.

Split-brain research has revealed that there are, in essence, two 'people' living inside each of us. One of the people is the conscious 'you', which is generally sited in the left hemisphere of the brain. The 'you', or left-brain, is good with words, is rational and logical, and can be regarded as the intellectual side of the composite person each of us is. The right-brain, by contrast, is generally silent, although on occasion it makes its presence felt, – in dreams, for example, or when we have hunches. Freud came close to describing the 'person' resident in the right-brain when he developed his idea of the unconscious.

The right-brain is not good at logic – at least, not logic as understood by the left-brain. The right-brain, therefore, is incapable of distinguishing between events which the left-brain categorizes as either 'probable' or 'improbable'; so far as the right-brain is concerned, things either happen or they do not. The left-brain is pretty certain that the sun will rise tomorrow; the right-brain regards each dawn as something fresh and new

Too many paranormal theorists have gone overboard about this. They say that the right-brain is capable of ranging through time, throwing heavy objects about, and so on, and then they sit back, satisfied, as if this provided some sort of total explanation. Of course, it does not. Assuming that the right-brain has these abilities, we still do not know *how* it can do these things.

Nevertheless, we can say with some degree of certainty that the right-brain is involved in most paranormal events – certainly in those described in the first part of this book, and possibly in most of those described in the second. Ignoring for the moment all the other evidence that this is the case, we can simply note that the 'improbability law' fits in so perfectly with our ideas about the patterns of right-brain thinking that it is hard to believe that it can be a mere coincidence.

Clearly we must be cautious as we approach the mysteries described in Part 1: we must keep both our gullibility and our scepticism in check as we evaluate the evidence before us. We must remember that the camera can lie – as, all too easily, can human beings! – but at the same time we must remember that our conscious, intellectual, left-brain self is a 'distinguished but elderly scientist' whose preconceptions and received notions may make him or her a poor judge of the evidence.

Care has been taken over the selection of mysteries to be discussed in Part 1. Famous 'mysteries' that have proved to be anything but are referred to only in passing – the case of the *Mary Celeste* is one such. Instead, the concentration is upon those events and phenomena that are particularly revealing, either because they are typical of a whole range of similar mysteries or because they are so far outside the normal limits of our understanding that they have a specific interest for exactly that reason.

One final caution. It may well be that, one day, you will find yourself in direct contact with a 'mystery'. Beware of accepting it too easily. That UFO you see could easily be a high-flying aircraft; the person who can bend cutlery using 'psychic' means may be only a conjurer. Never on any account part with any money if someone claims that he can contact your decreased sister or transport you to the planet Venus. Retain your scepticism at all times: 99 per cent of all apparent mysteries can be explained in rationalist terms, often quite easily.

On the other hand, the remaining one per cent cannot. These represent the true myseries.

Mysteries Of Mind And Body

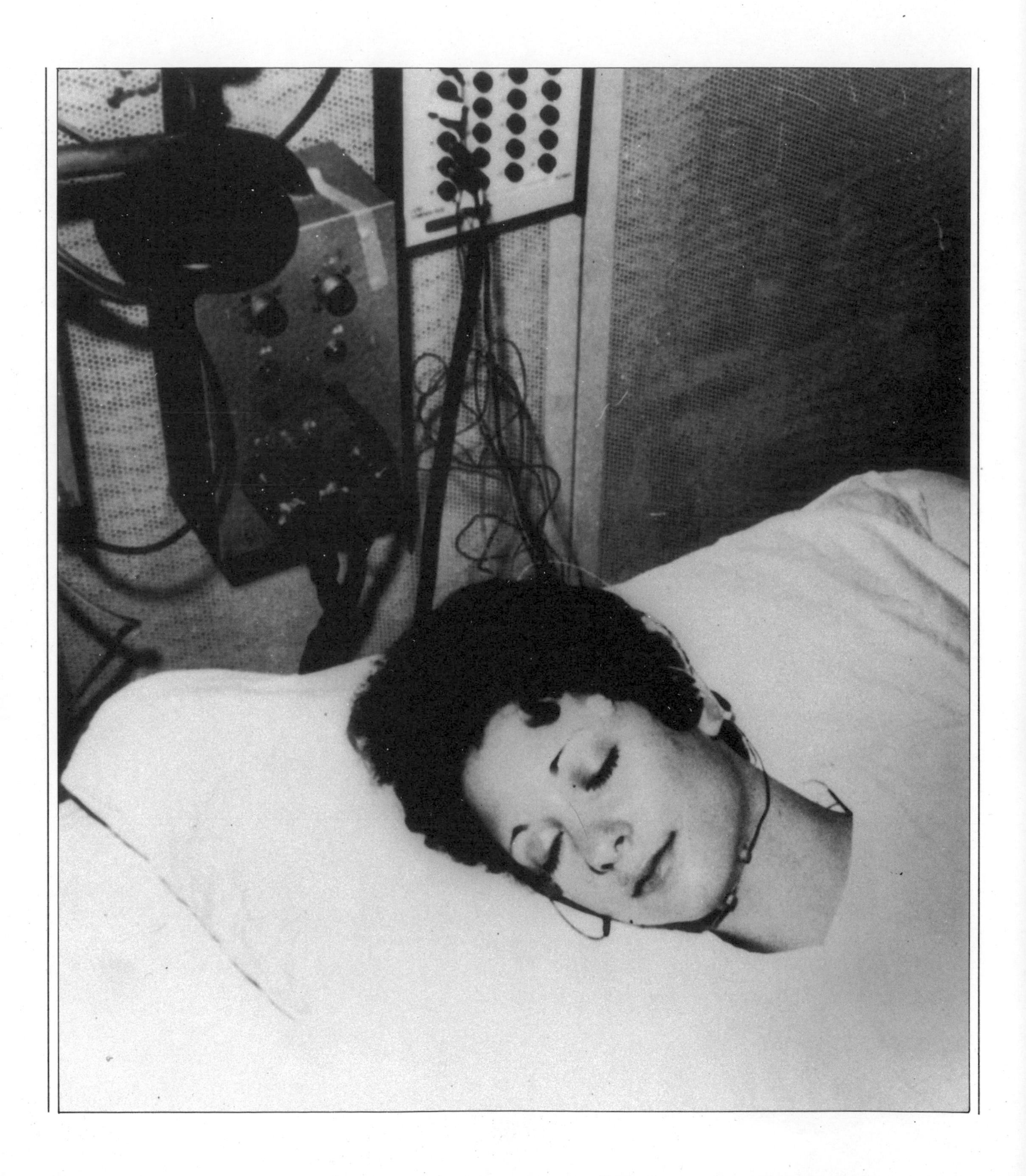

TELEPATHY

IN THE 1950s A small boy at a Scottish school discovered that he had forgotten his school-lunch ticket. He walked home to see if his mother were in. She was not, but, just as he was about to turn hungrily and disconsolately away, she appeared in the distance. She had been lunching in the university staff canteen nearby and had suddenly 'realized' that her son was at the family home and needed her. The 'message' had been strong enough for her to break off her lunch, say goodbye to her colleagues, and walk to the house.

Telepathy? It would seem so. Most people have had an experience of this sort at some time during their lives. Of course, in this instance it might simply have been that the mother unconsciously remembered that she had failed to give her son a lunch ticket, but such plausible explanations are far from frequently available. Many families are familiar with the phenomenon that, when one of them is in trouble, no matter how far away, the others somehow 'know'.

This sort of everyday telepathy is frequently reported, especially between family members, lovers and twins. However, formal experiments on telepathy have produced precious little by way of hard evidence. Normally cited are the experiments of J B and L E Rhine, which would seem to provide powerful evidence in favour of telepathy. Unfortunately, one cannot take these experiments at face value: the scientific controls used by the Rhines, while they improved over the years, were never better than slack. An

The husband-and-wife team of Professor J B **ABOVE** *and Dr L E Rhine* **RIGHT** *did pioneering work to investigate the phenomenon of telepathy. Their experiments produced some interesting results, but in recent years concern has been voiced about their methodology.* **LEFT** *An experiment underway on dream telepathy in the famous Maimonides Medical Center, Brooklyn, New York. The sleeping subject is wired up to an EEG (electroencephalogram) and a polygraph.*

early example will suffice. A 'psychic', A J Linzmayer, was tested early on by J B Rhine, and his rate of success when guessing the cards turned up by Rhine was astonishing; the odds against its having happened by chance were approximately 17 thousand million to one. Alas, these odds shorten quite a lot when the circumstances of the experiments are taken into account. In some, Rhine sat in the front of his car while Linzmayer sat in the back, having been firmly instructed not to look! As soon as more rigorous scientific controls were introduced Linzmayer's paranormal abilities curiously declined.

Yet telepathic experiences between people emotionally close are common, as we have noted. Rather like the example cited above was an experience had by the noted medium Eileen Garrett, who was born in Ireland but lived for much of her life in the United States. While living in London she had a curious dream about her daughter, who was away at boarding school. The daughter appeared in the dream, apologizing for the fact that she had not written the standard weekly letter home. She was suffering from some kind of chest fever and really was not up to the effort. The headmistress had initially berated her for failing to write, but now, seeing how ill she was, was being sympathetic. Sure enough, the weekly letter failed to arrive, and so Garrett telephoned the school. She spoke with the headmistress and discovered that indeed her daughter was in bed with a bad chest cold and had used this as an excuse, justified or otherwise, for declining to write home.

Oddly enough, while Garrett had various 'classic' telepathic experiences like this one, as soon as she went into the laboratory at Maimonides for testing by Ullman and Krippner her results became far less convincing. There are two possible reasons for this. Either she was vastly exaggerating the degree of coincidence between

TOP FAR LEFT: *An early form of random-number generator in use at the Rhines' laboratory. The subject was required to attempt to predict which of the four coloured lights would be the next to flash on.*
LEFT: *The medium Eileen Garrett*
SECOND FROM LEFT *investigating a haunted house; the exact site is unknown. Garrett recorded countless examples of her own apparently telepathic experiences. While her evidence is anecdotal rather than scientific, it cannot easily be discounted.*
ABOVE AND RIGHT: *Two views of a traditional test for telepathic abilities, using Zener cards. This experiment was conducted in 1940; the subject was Marion Barber, the tester Charles Stuart and the record-keeper J G Pratt. It is very clear that in these circumstances there was plenty of room for self-deception or even conscious fraud. Testing techniques have improved a little since then.*

her telepathic 'visions' and the reality, or – as has so often been claimed – whatever it is that is responsible for the paranormal declines to perform in a laboratory environment. (A third possibility is that as soon as people start to *try* to have paranormal experiences they find it impossible.)

Another astonishing example of telepathic dreaming was reported in 1884 by a Mrs Philip Crellin. She reported that

> three weeks ago, I was unable to sleep during the early hours of the night. I thought, amongst other things, of a rather comic piece of poetry which my husband used to repeat years ago I stuck at one line and could not recall it. However, I fell asleep, and three or four hours after awoke, to find it was time to rise. My husband, after a good night's rest . . . awoke also; he stretched out his hand towards me, and repeated the line I had failed to remember in the night, and which did not occupy my thoughts when I awoke in the morning.

It is conceivable that Mrs Crellin talked in her sleep, which might explain her husband's apparent telepathy, but this is rendered less than likely by the sheer volume of similar cases of sleeping spouses 'picking up' the thoughts of their awake partners. To quote just one more example, dating from about the same time as Mrs Crellin's experience, a certain Mrs Jean Fielding was lying awake while her husband snored and suddenly thought for the first time in years of a man called Harvey Brown, who had lived near to her girlhood home and who had been a very peripheral acquaintance. In the morning her husband mentioned that he had had a strange dream about this very same Harvey Brown.

Could such cases as these be merely coincidence? Possibly yes, but so many have been reported that it requires little knowledge of statistics to realize that the odds against pure coincidence are huge. However, we should be careful about the use of statistics by some paranormal investigators. Often you will read, for example, that an experimentee's ability to 'read' cards must be telepathic, because the odds against his or her 'hit rate' are so enormous. Sometimes, though, these vast odds are a result not of psychic powers but simply of the experimental technique. Imagine a card-reading experiment which starts off with 100 volunteers. After the first round of experiments the 50 lowest scores are discarded, and attention is focused on the others. The process is repeated until only a single individual is left – whose scores, not surprisingly, fly right in the face of the statistical odds. In this kind of experiment, there will obviously always be such an individual.

However, some statistical results provide genuine evidence in favour of the existence of telepathy. In 1942 Dr Gertrude Schmeidler performed a famous experiment. A group of volunteers were asked to 'read' cards. Before the experiment started she asked the people to declare whether they believed in the existence of telepathy; the sceptics she dubbed the 'goats' and the believers the 'sheep'. The 'sheep' produced results better than those to be expected through coincidence, but even more interesting was that the 'goats' produced significantly worse results. One possible explanation is that the left-brains of the sceptics overrode their right-brains; another possibility is that the 'sheep' believed in telepathy because they had already experienced it.

Many people – and possibly most – believe in telepathy, but the evidence is ambiguous, and certainly not as good as that in favour of some rather more outré 'mysteries' . . . as we shall see.

TOP: *Gertrude Schmeidler, the researcher who conducted the famous 'sheep and goats' experiment, one of the most significant in the history of research into ESP. The 'sheep' (believers) scored notably better than would have statistically been expected but, even more importantly, the scores of the 'goats' (non-believers) were substantially worse than they should have been had mere chance been involved.*

PRECOGNITION

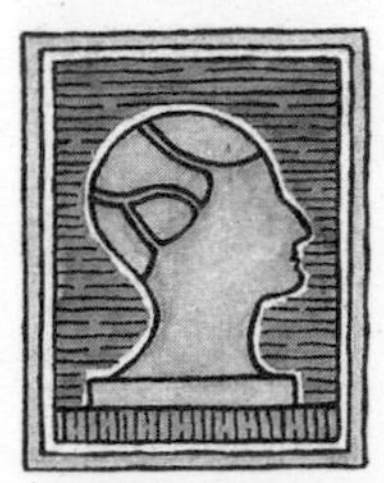

THERE ARE TWO WAYS of viewing precognition, the ability to detect or predict future events. One is that certain people are, quite simply, able to have sight of events that have not yet occurred. The other, by far the more controversial, is that our right-brains are capable of making minor modifications to the present and accurately foreseeing the more major future consequences of those changes. Both hypotheses are, of course, impossible to prove or disprove, and the same has to be said of the whole phenomenon of precognition itself, although the anecdotal evidence is overwhelming.

Precognition must be thought of in conjunction with the topic of coincidence. Imagine that you have the impression that you will be kicked by a horse tomorrow. If, as is very likely, you fail to be kicked by a horse, you will forget your foreboding. But if you are indeed kicked by a horse you will tell the world of your 'precognitive' experience. In other words, we remember coincidences but we are never aware of 'non-coincidences'. We must bear in mind, therefore, that a large part of the evidence for apparent precognition is necessarily explicable in terms of pure coincidence.

This argument can be turned on its head. Perhaps a lot of the things we regard as coincidences are in fact paranormal events. This was an idea that appealed to the psychoanalyst C G Jung, who produced a theory, 'synchronicity', to explain coincidences. The details are complex, but the overall notion was that there is some 'acausal principle' that operates in such a way that coincidental events occur that seem to *us* to have no causal link. By way of analogy, a fly sitting on the minute-hand of a clock might think it a strange coincidence that, every time the hand was vertical, bells started chiming; as far as the fly is concerned, there is an 'acausal principle' at work.

Jung, like the Austrian biologist Paul Kammerer, 'collected' coincidences. In a famous example, he noted one day that the number of his streetcar was the same as that of the ticket he had bought for the theatre the same evening; and he was surprised to find the number turning up during a telephone conversation he had that same day. The American psychic Alan Vaughan, not long after reading of this, was thinking about Jung's experience and looked at his own streetcar-ticket number: it was 096960, a number which can be read identically upside-down. On leaving the streetcar, he noticed that its number, too, was one that read the same when upside-down. Eagerly looking around for further examples of such synchronicity, he almost fell over an ashcan. Imagine his astonishment when he saw the name painted on it: JUNG!

A great deal of precognition comes about through dreams. However, some examples occur not just while the predictor is conscious but through a deliberate effort of will. Colin Wilson has cited the instance of a psychic named Orlop who, asked by the Israeli Parapsychological Society to give details of the occupant of a specific chair at one of their meetings some weeks hence, did so with a fair degree of accuracy. Kevin McClure, then of the Oxford University Society for Psychical Research, repeated the experiment, the psychic on this occasion being Robert Cracknell, and once again the results were far better than anything that could be explained away as coincidence. Psychic detective Gerard Croiset has likewise had a fair degree of success in such trials.

ABOVE: *Gerard Croiset, the celebrated psychic detective. In some cases his results have been astonishingly successful; in others they have been the exact opposite.*

To describe these experiments as 'controlled' would be to overstate matters; nevertheless it is hard to find any other explanation for them than that the phenomenon of precognition genuinely exists. Here, of course, our 'model' of precognition – that it is not so much that people predict the future, more that their right-brains act in such a way as to mould it – runs into a number of problems. It is very hard to see how the right-brain of either Orlop or Cracknell could have 'arranged' for a particular stranger to be in a particular place at a particular time. This may well be a fault in the 'model'; equally, it may be that the right-brain is capable of operating with a subtlety incomprehensible to the conscious left-brain.

Some people have made international reputations out of their supposed precognitive abilities. Notable among these are the so-called 'psychic detectives', such as Croiset, Cracknell and Peter Hurkos. These people have claimed the ability to handle objects and thereby detect their histories (an ability technically termed 'psychometry'). It is hard to establish the success rate of such enterprises, but some of the results have been startling, to say the least. For example, when Peter Hurkos was called in to help in the investigation of the Boston Strangler case, he handled the clothing of some of the victims and then gave very precise details of the person responsible for the killings. His predictions, which included bizarre personal habits, were absolutely spot-on, right down to the address – but the individual concerned was only a minor sex offender, not the murderer.

How did this come about? There is no real reason to believe that the relevant underwear had been handled by the sex offender (although Hurkos himself wonders if there was a miscarriage of justice). It seems possible that what Hurkos did was to predict the arrest of the fetishist and the discovery of the objects he had collected. If so, Hurkos' contact with the underwear may have sparked off something rather different to psychometry: it may have concentrated his right-brain on the subject of fetishism, with the result that it was able to forecast the arrest of a particular sex offender – which arrest, of course, it actually *caused*.

Any sensible discussion of precognition must take account of our current scientific understanding of the nature of time. This differs quite substantially from the popular notion of time, which suggests that it simply 'flows'. Time to the scientist is a dimension, to be considered alongside the dimensions of length, width and depth. We can manipulate events within the three common dimensions; so it seems feasible that we can also manipulate things within the fourth.

Also we view time as being an *ordering* of events: the past precedes the present which precedes the future. We talk of the 'arrow of time' and assume that it can never do otherwise. Yet this is not necessarily the case. For example, if there are in distant parts of the universe galaxies made up of antimatter, rather than matter, then according to some scientists the 'arrow of time' there must point in the opposite 'direction'.

Finally we must remember tachyons. It is often stated that Einstein's theory of relativity says that nothing can travel faster than the speed of light. This is an erroneous simplification. The implication of relativity is that nothing material can travel *at* the speed of light. The mathematics of relativity allows for particles that *always* travel faster than light – and, indeed, cannot be slowed down to sub-light velocities. If tachyons exist, and there is some reason to believe they do, then the mathematics is such that they must be travelling 'backwards' in time.

Time is, then, not quite the simple thing we perceive it to be. If, as science suggests, time can do things like run 'backwards', scientists must accept that precognition is a very real possibility. Whether people capable of it are, as it were, unconscious tachyon-detectors, or whether their right-brains are capable of manipulating the future – or whether there is some totally different explanation – is something about which we can, at this stage, only guess. However, the weight of evidence – anecdotal and bitty although it may be – is currently in favour of precognition.

PARANORMAL DREAMING

SAMUEL CLEMENS HAD A curiously frightening dream in 1858, when he was 23, long before he became famous as Mark Twain. At the time, he and his brother, Henry, were making a living working on the Mississippi riverboats. In his dream Samuel saw his brother's body laid out in the family living-room in a metal coffin supported between two chairs; a bouquet of white flowers, with a single red flower in the centre, lay on the corpse's breast. The dream so affected Samuel that when he awoke he told his sister that it was his sincere belief that Henry was dead.

In fact, Henry proved still to be very much alive. But some weeks later Henry was one of many people killed when the boiler of the boat on which he was working exploded. His remains were rescued and, thanks to the ladies of Memphis, who took pity on his youth and made a collection, were laid out in an expensive metal coffin, rather than a cheap wooden one, as with all the other victims of the tragedy. Samuel's first sight of his brother's body reflected precisely the scene of his dream – except for the fact that it was in someone else's living-room and that there was no bouquet of flowers on Henry's chest. Just then, however, a woman entered the room and placed a wreath of white flowers, with a red one at the centre, exactly where Samuel had seen it in his dream.

This startling account of precognitive dreaming is widely reported. But is the story in fact true? The sole source is Twain's *Autobiography*, which actually consists of a chaotic collection of disjointed ramblings, most of them taken down by friends to his dictation. One of those friends frankly described much of the contents as straight fiction. So the story may have been nothing more than a 'good tale' devised by Twain in his senility. It *might* be true, but we have no way of telling.

This is a not infrequent conclusion when studying records of paranormal dreams. There are several reasons for this. One is that people often simply lie, pretending in the aftermath of a real event that they dreamed about it beforehand.

TOP LEFT: *Peter Hurkos, like Croiset a psychic detective, played a notable part in the famous Boston Strangler case. Although he was unable to identify the murderer (Albert de Salvo), his results were so curious that they cannot be coincidental.*

RIGHT: *Samuel Clemens ('Mark Twain') who in later life claimed to have had a precognitive dream about the tragic death of his brother.*

Far more subtle – and far harder to detect because there is no deliberate deceit involved – is 'reading back'. Imagine that you dreamed one night that you were flying, and the next day you fell down the stairs – in other words, 'flew' There is a similarity between the dream and the reality, enough of a similarity that you will very likely 'misremember' your dream, your unconscious mind altering its memories of the dream until the details tally in full detail with the reality.

It is worth stressing that 'reading back' is not a conscious effect; it will happen unless you take steps to avoid it (such as keeping a dream diary). The phenomenon makes life difficult for researchers because the dreamer is quite genuinely convinced that his or her dream accurately foretold the future.

CICERO

A third difficulty in evaluating paranormal dreams is that 'the story improves with the telling'. For example, we read that Cicero once dreamed that he saw a youth being lowered on a golden chain from the skies to stand in a temple door. The next morning he was introduced by Julius Caesar to the youth of his dream – Gaius Octavius, who was later to become Augustus, Rome's first emperor. Indeed, Augustus was responsible for having Cicero put to death, and our first account of this dream dates from a time some while after this event. It seems almost certainly to have been a tale which was concocted by later historians. The dreams interpreted by Joseph in *Genesis XII* are probably a product of similar inventiveness by chroniclers (although there was indeed an important seer, possibly called Joseph, in Egypt at that time).

LEFT: *A bust of Cicero, who was widely reported to have had a precognitive dream identifying the future Emperor Augustus. However, the first account of this dates from some while after the accession of Augustus and the death of Cicero, so there is every reason to be sceptical about the story.* **ABOVE:** *One of many contemporary prints showing the failed actor John Wilkes Booth assassinating Abraham Lincoln in 1865. Thirty years later Ward Hill Lamon would recount how the president had dreamed of his forthcoming assassination.*

This urge to embellish a good tale causes investigators problems even when dealing with events as recent as the 19th century. One of the most famous precognitive dreams was recounted by Abraham Lincoln to a circle of friends in April, 1865. Lincoln dreamed that he was in bed at the White House when he heard the sounds of mourning filling the air. He got out of bed and went to find out what was going on.

> . . . I kept on until I arrived at the East Room, which I entered. There I met with a sickening surprise. Before me was a catafalque, on which rested a corpse wrapped in funeral vestments. Around it were stationed soldiers who were acting as guards; and there was a throng of people, some gazing mournfully upon the corpse, whose face was covered, others weeping pitifully. 'Who is dead in the White House?' I demanded of one of the soldiers. 'The President,' was his answer; 'he was killed by an assassin!'

Unfortunately, the details of the dream were not noted down at the time. The first written version of it appeared in 1895 in *Recollections of Lincoln* by Ward Hill Lamon, one of the company to whom Lincoln had recounted the dream. Why, one wonders, did Lamon not tell the world about it the moment Lincoln was assassinated? The answer is depressingly obvious.

Even if the tale is true, it hardly stands as a great example of precognitive dreaming, because Lincoln was anyway much concerned about the danger of being assassinated. This comment, however, does not apply to some dreams about other assassinations. About ten days before the murder of the British prime minister, Spencer Perceval, in 1812 a banker called John Williams dreamed that he was in the lobby of the House of Commons when he saw 'a small man, dressed in a blue coat and white waistcoat', whom he was told was Perceval. Williams saw this person shot dead by a man in a 'snuff-coloured coat with metal buttons'. Williams awoke and told his wife about the dream; she told him not to be so silly and to go back to sleep – which he did, only to experience the same dream twice more. Over the next day or two he told several people about the dreams, which had affected him considerably. It was only two days after Perceval's death that Williams heard about the murder. Even then, he seems not to have been overly impressed until, some weeks later, he was in London and came across a cheap drawing of the dramatic scene: all the details were exactly as in his dream, notably the clothing worn by Perceval and his murderer, John Bellingham.

There are two important points here. First, Williams told a number of people about the dreams, and later they willingly substantiated his account. Second, living far from London, Williams had little clue as to whom his dream referred – he thought of Perceval as chancellor of the exchequer, little realizing that he was prime minister, too – and so it would have been difficult for him to invent the details. It is possible that the description of the clothing is a product of unconscious 'reading back' on seeing the cheap drawing, but the overall burden of the dream cannot be so easily discounted. There is every reason to believe that this was a genuine precognitive dream.

The most famous assassinations of this century are probably those of John and Robert Kennedy. In the aftermath of both murders, people all over the world claimed to have 'previewed' the killings. The best known claimant is Jeane Dixon; unfortunately, her story does not stand up to rigorous investigation. Rather more interesting is a dream had by the American seer Alan Vaughan which seemed to predict the assassination of Robert Kennedy. The dream is interesting for both its similarities to and differences from the actuality. The circumstantial details are strikingly similar in both dream and reality (Vaughan kept a dream diary, so that we know these details were not later additions). For example, in the dream the shooting took place in a hotel lobby (or something similar) off which there was a roomful

TOP: *Jeane Dixon, probably the most famous of modern psychics. She is recorded as having had a precognitive vision of the assassination of John F Kennedy. While the vision she had was interesting, and possibly indeed precognitive, later writers have tended to 'gild the lily' when describing it.* **RIGHT:** *The Titanic being towed out of Southampton Docks preparatory to her fatal departure in 1912. Stories concerning passengers who cancelled at the last moment because of precognitive dreams are legion. It is difficult now to evaluate these accounts, but certainly there were many last-minute cancellations.*

of young people, and this proved indeed to be the case. However, according to the dream Kennedy was shot by a single bullet fired by an assassin hidden behind a grating in the ceiling, whereas in reality Sirhan Sirhan was in the lobby in front of Kennedy. Oddly, though, the coroner's report indicated that Kennedy died from a single bullet fired only a few inches from the back of his head. Could it be, asks Vaughan, that his dream was actually a more accurate version of events than the police reports and the video tapes? If Vaughan is ever shown to have been correct, then the case for paranormal dreaming will have been proved.

Most disasters attract claims of precognitive dreaming. To judge by the tales told after the sinking of the *Titanic*, it is surprising that there were any passengers on board. None of the claims can now be sensibly evaluated (although, interestingly, one of the claimed precognitive dreamers was the novelist Graham Greene, then aged five). The same sort of thing happened before the 1966 Aberfan disaster, when an avalanche of slurry in Wales killed 144 people, mainly children. The psychologist J C Barker and the journalist Peter Fairley put out an appeal asking for examples of precognitive dreams. Of the 76 reports received an astonishingly high number, 22 (29 per cent), were backed up by supporting statements from people who had been told of the dream by the dreamer *before the actual event took place*. Barker and Fairley were inspired to set up an organization called the Premonitions Bureau, with the aim of collecting accounts of such precognition in order to obviate or at least ameliorate further disasters. The results were inconclusive, and the experiment ended within a few years.

A rather more scientific study along similar lines had been set up in 1947 by the British psychiatrist, Alice Buck. She and her colleagues kept detailed dream diaries and then compared their records to see if 'partial predictions' could be pieced together, jigsaw-fashion, to produce something more definite. Their most impressive series of results came in 1954-55, when they made what seemed to be quite startlingly accurate predictions of the various Comet aircraft disasters. The most fascinating part of this series of dreams is that, with hindsight, a lot of the dream-images seem to point at metal fatigue in the Comet aircraft; only later was it discovered that the disasters did indeed spring from the fact that the Comet was, by the nature of its design, prone to vibration-induced metal fatigue, the direct cause of the accidents.

Dream-premonitions of deaths can take strange forms. In the early 1980s a Devon widow named Audrey Atkinson dreamed of a death and a funeral *cortège*, and over the next few weeks quietly assumed that 'her number was up'. When in due course the circumstances of the funeral were 'replayed' in real life it proved that the person who had died was a man whom she had not known but who had lived a few doors away from her.

Looking through the files of paranormal dreams, it is immediately obvious that they score their most resounding successes when dealing with trivia. An astonishing example concerns a 1942 dream of Laura Dale, of the American Society for Psychical Research. Her dream involved a dog and an exploding vacuum-cleaner, and she told other people about it simply because it was so outrageous. However, a few days later she was at the movies and saw a cartoon involving, believe it or not, a dog and an exploding vacuum-cleaner. If this was precognition at work, and it certainly seems like it, one can only ask: *why*?

Trivial seeming too, were the precognitive dreams of John Godley, later Lord Kilbracken. In 1946 he began to dream about being at horse-races, and soon he noticed parallels between the races of his dreams and those which in fact later took place. By use of a little detective work (typically, the names of the horses in his dreams did not exactly match up with those of their real-life counterparts), he found that he could earn himself a highly useful ancillary income. Over the years Lord Kilbracken's 'powers' waned somewhat, but he nevertheless became a very successful newspaper tipster and there have been a number of other cases like Godley's.

Prediction through dreams – oneiromancy – certainly seems to occur, not very often, not very reliably, and rarely unambiguously. How can we explain this?

The most famous attempt to do this has been that of J W Dunne, who in *An Experiment with Time* and later books put forward his idea of 'serial time'. This is a complicated notion, but in essence he said that, for prediction to be possible, the future must in some sense 'already have happened'. He therefore posited two different 'sorts' of time: 'Time 1', which is our everyday sort of time, and 'Time 2', relative to which the 'flow' of 'Time 1' is measured – rather as you might measure the speed of a river current relative to the river's banks.

He suggested that the dreaming mind naturally operates in 'Time 2', from which vantage-point it can see the whole of 'Time 1', both future and past. The idea has its philosophical attractions, but it suffers from a grave disadvantage. If indeed there is a 'Time 2', then what is *it* measured against? Presumably 'Time 3', itself measured against 'Time 4' . . . and so *adinfinitum*.

A fashionable explanation of precognitive dreams is that they are spawned from our right-brains, which are capable of performing all sorts of acts that our left-brains consider impossible – i.e., paranormal. Although interesting, this theory is not very helpful, in that we are still left with no clue as to how precognition could possibly work under these circumstances.

A more reasonable suggestion (although superficially a much less likely one) is that it is not so much that our right-brains *predict* the future as that they *mould* it. If indeed the right-brain is responsible for poltergeist activity (*see* page 44), then there seems little reason why it cannot make a few small changes to present reality which have vast consequences days or years in the future. In other words, it may well be that our dreams are not so much warning us of future events as informing us of the end-results of the set of circumstances which our right-brain has just set in train.

A rather different possibility concerns patterns. We are all familiar with hunches – the 'everyday paranormal experience'. A reasonable explanation of these is that the right-brain has drawn together elements and trends unobserved by our conscious left-brain, and has extrapolated from these the inevitable – or, at least, probable – outcome. Perhaps the same process is responsible for the fact that through dreams we seem to be given, on occasion, a rather more definitive statement of likely future events.

Clairvoyance

Clairvoyance and telepathy would seem to be inextricably linked and it is an area where there has been much investigation.

These kinds of experiences, which relate to the sub-conscious, often manifest themselves in dreams.

In the late 19th century Miss R H Busk had a curious dream:

> I dreamt that I was walking in a wood in my father's place in Kent, in a spot well known to me, where there was sand under the firs; I stumbled over some objects, which proved to be the heads, left protruding, of some ducks buried in the sand. The idea impressed me as so comical that I fortunately mentioned it at breakfast next morning. . .

For students of clairvoyance this was indeed a fortunate occurrence, for Miss Busk went on to relate that

> only an hour later it happened that the old bailiff of the place came up for some instructions unexpectedly, and as he was leaving he said he must tell us a strange thing that had happened: there had been a robbery in the farmyard, and some stolen ducks had been found buried in the sand, with their heads protruding, in the very spot where I had seen the same.

This dream is possibly the best evidence that there is indeed such a phenomenon as clairvoyance – the ability to perceive things 'at a distance'. It is a little-known fact that foxes, when stealing poultry, will on occasion bury the unfortunate birds up to their necks, one at a time, going back for the next victim. Clearly this fact was quite unknown to Miss Busk; from her account, it seems to have been unknown to the bailiff as well. It is hard to think of a simpler explanation than that, in her dream, Miss Busk was experiencing clairvoyance.

It is difficult to draw the line between clairvoyance, precognition, telepathy and OOBEs (out-of-body experiences). Miss Busk's experience could be interpreted in several ways. Perhaps she 'saw in advance' the tale the bailiff would tell her; perhaps she had telepathic contact, as she slept in the early hours of the morning, with the people discovering the ducks; perhaps she had an OOBE, whereby she actually visited the site. As with so much of the paranormal, definitive explanations are not easy. All we can say is that, unless Miss Busk was lying through her teeth, she had a paranormal experience of some kind – and 'clairvoyance' is as good a tag as any to apply to it.

As with precognition, we find that the vast majority of clairvoyant experiences concern matters of the utmost triviality. There are no records of clairvoyants perceiving, shall we say, the build-up to the Russian invasion of Afghanistan, yet there are lots of records of curiosities such as Miss Busk's apparently clairvoyant dream about the ducks.

The Seven Spinal Chakras, by M K Scralian. In 1971 this picture was projected in front of the audience at a Grateful Dead concert, and all present were asked to concentrate on it. The aim was to see if the psychic Malcolm Bessent would be able to 'pick up' the picture in his dreams. In fact, he gave a reasonable description. However, an even better description was given from her dreams by Felicia Parise, a young psychic who had been operating as a 'control' for Bessent.

Research into clairvoyance has been going on apace in the United States during the 1980s. Some of this has been academic (does it really happen?), while some of it has been commercial (at least one company will give you psychic advice as to what to do with your stocks and shares). Pioneers in the field were Montague Ullman and Stanley Krippner at the Maimonides Medical Center. In 1971 they asked the rock group, The Grateful Dead, to cooperate in an experiment. The band was giving a series of six concerts 50 miles or more from where the British clairvoyant Malcolm Bessent would be sleeping. Each night the audience were asked to concentrate for a short while on a picture projected behind the band, and to try to 'send' it to Bessent. The night they showed a painting by M K Scralian called *The Seven Spinal Chakras* Bessent's description was very close indeed. However, unknown to anyone except the experimenters, there was a control being run: Felicia Parise, who was showing signs of being an interesting clairvoyant, likewise recorded her dreams for the Maimonides team. Two days after *The Seven Spinal Chakras* had been projected, but long before the results had been correlated and the information passed back, she came out with a description of the painting that is quite chilling in its accuracy.

Another startling example of clairvoyance came in an experiment conducted by Harold Puthoff and Russell Targ at the Stanford Research Institute. Here the 'guinea pig' was Ingo Swann, who has since become an internationally renowned psychic. Swann was given an accurate statement of the latitude and longitude of a site and told to describe what he saw there. He said that he could see a mountainous island, and was promptly told that he was wrong: the latitude and longitude indicated a part of the Indian Ocean where there were no islands. It was only later that the experimenters discovered that there was indeed an island in exactly that situation, and that at its eastern end rose mountains.

It is worth noting an example of apparent clairvoyance that concerned something other than trivia. In World War II John Barnett was stationed in Nigeria, and at the height of the U-boat campaign his wife, Muriel, went out to join him. One night he was startled out of his sleep, sat bolt upright in bed, and watched the play of bright, flickering lights all over his bedroom walls. Some days later, when his wife arrived, he described the experience to her. It turned out that, while he was having this 'vision', she was undergoing the convoy's sole U-boat alert, standing in her life-saver on deck in the middle of the night, watching the searchlights of the destroyers flickering on the water.

Clairvoyance, telepathy or coincidence? It is very hard to say. Coincidence is a possibility, but the synchronism is not easy to explain, and neither is the precise nature of the 'vision'. Really, we are left with a choice between telepathy and clairvoyance; and the evidence is such that clairvoyance seems the better option.

Scrying is the use of an object – such as a bowl of water or a crystal ball – as a way of focusing your attention in order to assist clairvoyance. It has to be said right at the outset that scrying has for centuries been the refuge of knaves and rogues intent on impressing their gullible fellows very often for personal gain.

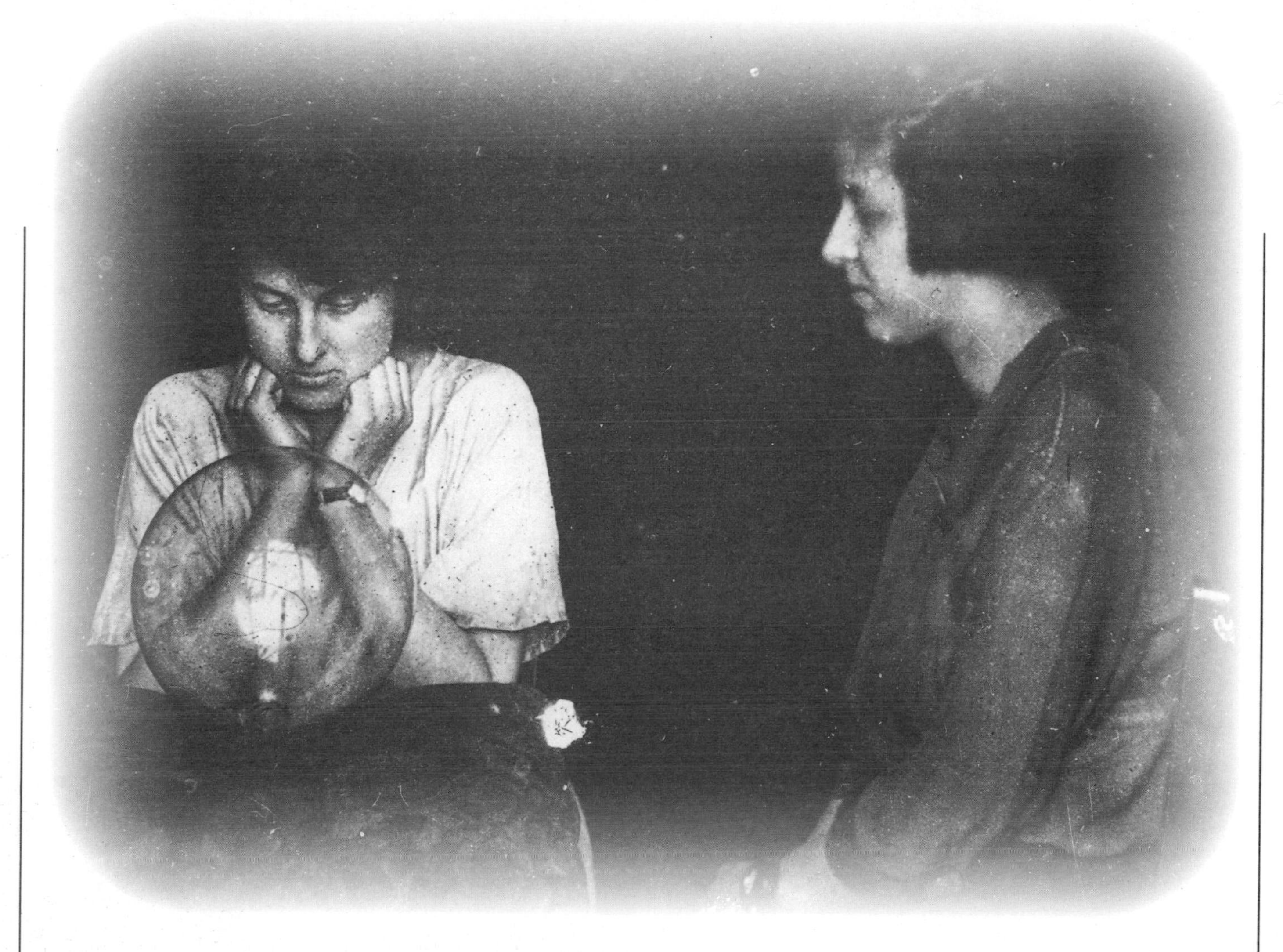

The classic case is that of Edward Kelley, the long-time companion of the great 16th-century mystic and polymath, John Dee.

Kelley claimed to have been given a magic crystal by what he called 'angels', from whom he could now receive messages through staring at the crystal. Dee spent a number of years noting down Kelley's dictation, which was, on the face of it, gibberish. However, Dee was able to 'decode' the language used, which he called 'Enochian'. Strangely, this language has a consistent syntax and grammar.

It may be that Dee's subconscious was responsible for all the notes, or it may be that Kelley was an extremely clever trickster; Dee came to the latter conclusion when Kelley's 'angels' announced that he, Kelley, should sleep with Dee's wife!

Russell Targ **FAR LEFT** *and* Harold Puthoff **LEFT** *whose work together has done much to bring a new respectability to studies of clairvoyance and other forms of* ESP. **ABOVE:** *The traditional image of the clairvoyant staring into the crystal ball. The use of an object – whether it be a crystal ball, a pool of water, or whatever – in clairvoyance is technically termed scrying, and has been practised for untold centuries. The popular notion that it is the object that 'does the magic' is of course erroneous. The most likely explanation is that it acts merely as a focus for the clairvoyant's right-brain.*

Assuming that people are capable of clairvoyance, then it is fair to say that the ability is obviously closely related to that of precognition. In fact, it is tempting to suggest that clairvoyance actually *is* precognition. For example, J W Dunne, in his famous 'experiment with time', had a dream which, he was convinced, told him of the occurrence of the Mont Pelée disaster of 1902. In his dream he was 'told' that 4,000 people had been killed. Much later the news of the disaster reached South Africa, where Dunne then lived. The subsidiary headline of the newspaper report he read ran, PROBABLE LOSS OF OVER 40,000 LIVES, and he read '40,000' as '4,000'. It was only about 15 years later that he noticed his misreading.

So was Dunne experiencing clairvoyance or precognition? The evidence suggests the latter, because in fact the newspaper report was quite wrong about the number of casualties. It is much more likely that Dunne foresaw himself reading the newspaper account than that he had a direct clairvoyant dream of the disaster as it happened.

From this incident, and a host of others in the literature, we get the impression that clairvoyance is not what it seems: rather than being 'far-seeing' it is the precognitive ability to foresee information that one will later receive. Of course, there is something of a time-loop at work here: Dunne would not have been so impressed by the newspaper story had it not been for his dream, and his dream would not have etched itself so firmly into his consciousness had it not been for its later apparent vindication by the newspaper report of the actuality.

What then of scrying? Whether it helps the individual to be precognitive or clairvoyant, how does it function? The probability is that the object gazed at – be it a crystal ball, tealeaves or whatever – acts much in the same way as the swinging watch of the hypnotist: it allows the left-brain to 'switch off' so that the right-brain can take over. In other words, the scryer is engaging in an exercise of self-hypnosis, yet the left-brain is remaining alert enough to record the images transmitted by the right-brain. That this might be the case is certainly evident to anyone who has been hypnotized. The experience is most curious: although your left-brain is conscious throughout all of what is going on, it 'takes a holiday', as it were, and allows the words of the hypnotist to enter the right-brain directly, without any prior intellectual analysis.

There are other reasons to believe that scrying is a form of self-hypnosis. Experiments done over the past decade or two have used hypnosis to allow people to recall their (apparent) previous incarnations, while people in the dream-state – which is, in certain ways, like the hypnotic trance – have, like Dunne, been capable of some form or another of extrasensory perception (ESP). It is rather alarming to think that people 'reading' tealeaves or looking at Tarot cards are actually – unless they are charlatans – hypnotizing themselves, yet this seems the most likely explanation.

RIGHT: *A volunteer submits to a Ganzfeld (GZ) experiment. The conditions represent a half-way stage between normality and total sensory deprivation; white noise is played through the headphones, and the soothing red light is filtered and diffused through halved table-tennis balls fixed in front of the subject's eyes. In a distant room a person acting as 'transmitter' concentrates on a picture. The completely relaxed volunteer speaks in steam-of-consciousness fashion about the mental images that appear. A number of comparative tests have been done between groups of volunteers in the GZ state and control groups, and the results have been startling; consistently the GZ volunteers have scored substantially higher in apparently 'picking up' details of the 'transmitted' pictures.*

Out-of-Body Experiences

Out-of-body experiences, universally known as OOBEs (to rhyme with 'rubies'), work two ways. First there are the experiences countless people have had of seeming to leave their body temporarily, either to visit the afterlife, as has been frequently reported in cases of people who have recovered from near-death, or simply to travel far from their physical bodies. Second there are instances of people appearing – miles away from where they actually are – in front of their friends or acquaintances. One can explain the former type of experience fairly simply in terms of orthodox psychology; the latter is a little less easy to explain.

The celebrated American psychic Jeane Dixon has told of an experience of the latter type. She lived many miles from her elderly father. One night, she reports, she woke from 'an unusually deep sleep' to find a spectre of her father by her bedside. He told her that he'd come to say farewell, and encouraged her to keep up her psychic work, because it was doing good. As you might expect, when Dixon telephoned her sister shortly afterwards, she discovered that her father had just died.

There are countless examples of dying parents coming to say a last farewell to their offspring, usually in dreams, but often enough to a person who is wide-awake – or, at least, a person who *thinks* he or she is wide-awake. The distinction is an important one. A person who is on the verge of falling asleep is capable of having so-called 'hypnagogic' dreams, and these have a strikingly high level of apparent reality. Most of us have had the experience of half falling asleep while reading. The plot of our book gets more and more curious until we finally realize what is going on and switch the light out. This is a very mild form of hypnagogic dream. People who are regular hypnagogic dreamers will tell you how vividly 'real' the visions are. (Both Robert Louis Stevenson and Edgar Allan Poe deliberately encouraged their hypnagogic dreams in order to get ideas for stories.) Analogous to hypnagogic dreams are hypnopompic ones, experienced just as you awake: Dixon's experience sounds very like a hypnopompic dream, a hypothesis supported by the facts that, first, she knew her father was dying, and, second, she herself mentions that she had just awoken.

Perhaps one can give a similar explanation of the curious OOBE case involving the novelists John Cowper Powys and

Theodore Dreiser. The two had dined together at Dreiser's home in New York, and as Powys departed he mysteriously told Dreiser that he would visit him later that night. Dreiser thought, quite naturally, that Powys was joking. However, a couple of hours afterwards, Dreiser suddenly saw Powys standing at the door of his room. He moved towards Powys, asking rather crossly how he had done the 'trick', but the spectre disappeared. The real-life Powys, on being telephoned, refused to make any comment on the matter.

It is tempting to say that all that happened was that Dreiser, having registered his friend's somewhat curious farewell remark, was drowsing and had a hypnagogic dream; Powys's refusal to comment could then simply be seen as a facet of his known fondness for being enigmatic. Yet to Dreiser the spectral 'visit' of Powys was something very real: he did not doubt for a moment that his friend was actually, in some form, there. It is a very great pity that there was no one with Dreiser at the time, because then we could establish whether or not this was an OOBE rather than a hypnagogic dream.

Experiences such as Dixon's and Dreiser's can be explained as hypnagogic dreaming, but there are other possibilities. One is that their 'visitors' deliberately projected themselves out of their material bodies. Another is that the 'visited' somehow drew the projections out of the 'visitors'. In neither case have we any evidence that the 'visitor' knew of the phenomenon.

The other type of OOBE is that in which the person directly involved knows that he has left his body. In 1863 S R Wilmot sailed from England to rejoin his family in the United States. He shared a cabin with one William Tait. One night Wilmot 'saw' his wife, clad only in her nightie, enter the cabin, hesitate when she saw someone else there, and then conquer her shyness to come over to his bunk and kiss him.

It is not unnatural that spouses separated for a long time should have such visions. What startled Wilmot, however, was that in the morning Tait accused him of being a rakehell: he too had seen this scantily clad woman entering the cabin and behaving with a certain lack of decorum. To make the matter even odder, on his arrival in New York Wilmot was asked by his wife whether he remembered the 'visit'; she described exactly what had happened, and on subsequent questioning was able to give details of the general layout of the cabin.

Various scientific experiments have been done on OOBEs, notably by Harold Puthoff and Russell Targ. The conclusion from all such tests has to be that OOBEs do genuinely occur. Why they should, and how, is a matter of mystery.

LEFT: *One of the most astonishing accounts of an OOBE concerns the two writers Theodore Dreiser and John Cowper Powys, the latter apparently projecting his image to visit the former. In this unusual photograph we see Dreiser contemplating a bust of Powys.* **ABOVE, LEFT:** *Robert Louis Stevenson and* **RIGHT:** *Edgar Allan Poe, two writers who deliberately exploited the visions which they saw in the hypnagogic state in order to create their fictions.*

TIMESLIPS

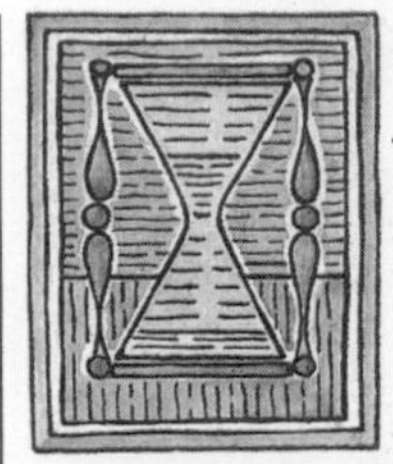

IN 1911 ELEANOR JOURDAIN and Charlotte Moberly, two Oxford dons, published the book *An Adventure*. In it they recounted a curious experience which they had shared when visiting the Palace of Versailles in 1901. Wandering through the gardens, they found themselves in 1789, just before the downfall of the French monarchy. They encountered people dressed in the clothing of that age who talked of the current (1789) political situation. Somehow the two women had slipped back in time. There are rationalist explanations. For example, there

was a fancy-dress party in Versailles in 1894, and it is possible that the two women stumbled into it. However, there is a big difference between 1894 and 1901.

Reports of such phenomena are rare, but they are convincing. Take the example of Jane O'Neill, who in 1973 suffered a severe shock (she helped free people trapped after a particularly nasty traffic accident). After this she began to have a number of paranormal experiences, the most significant of which concerned a visit to Fotheringhay Church, England. She found herself particularly fascinated by one picture, and later mentioned this fact to the friend who had been with her. To her amazement, the friend said that she had seen no such picture. Mrs O'Neill was concerned enough to make some enquiries, and eventually found that she had 'seen' the interior of the church as it had been in the 1500s. Somehow, she had 'travelled' back several hundred years.

Such accounts are reminiscent of presumed 'reincarnatory' dreams, in which people seem to recall their previous existences. An intriguing experiment in this field was carried out by a group headed by the Australian writer, G M Glaskin, during the 1970s. Typically, the experimenter would lie down, shoes off, and have his or her ankles and pineal region (the centre of the forehead) massaged by assistants; then one of the assistants would instruct the experimenter to go through a number of psychic exercises before returning to a 'past life'.

The results were astonishing: the experimenters had stunningly vivid experiences of what they believed to be earlier incarnations. One, a bisexual, was fellated superbly by a male prostitute in a Roman 'pleasure palace', yet his real-life body failed to show the signs of his experience. Others believed that, as well as reliving previous incarnations, they had travelled forward in time to experience future ones. One of Glaskin's own 'journeys' was of particular interest in that, some while later, he visited the British Museum and was able to pinpoint his vision as having occurred about 5,000 years earlier in the Faiyum, Egypt. He had had not the slightest interest in Egyptology before making this discovery, and so concludes that he genuinely experienced a few hours of life in a past age.

Is it possible to slip back into a previous era? According to our modern understanding of the physical laws that define the universe, it is very difficult indeed to 'visit' the future and equally difficult to *affect* the past. However, there is nothing in modern science that prohibits merely 'visiting' the past.

An exciting piece of evidence – and one that is so far totally lacking – might be an historical record of a stranger appearing for a short while in, say, the 17th century, sporting a Mohican cut and clad in blue jeans. It is possible that there are indeed such records, as we shall see when we look at cases of 'appearing people', but as yet we have to conclude that the evidence is indicative rather than compelling. Nevertheless, the Misses Moberly and Jourdain are unlikely candidates for hoaxers, and anyway they ran the risk of losing their professional respectability by publishing their accounts of what they seem genuinely to have believed to be a timeslip. Until we have evidence to the contrary, we have to take their accounts at face value.

ABOVE LEFT: *Le Petit Trianon at Versailles.* **RIGHT:** *Fotheringhay Church, seen over the waters of the River Nene. It was here in 1973 that Jane O'Neill experienced what seems to have been a timeslip, seeing the interior of the church as it had been several hundred years before.*

Eleanor Jourdain **LEFT** and Charlotte Moberly **ABOVE** *the two respectable English gentlewomen who seemed to travel back in time by over a century during a visit to Versailles. No one has yet offered a convincing rationalist explanation for their experience.*

REINCARNATION

DESPITE OCCASIONAL NEWSPAPER REPORTS to the contrary, depressingly few Western scientists are remotely interested in the paranormal: most regard it as either a load of nonsense or, at best, something totally outside their own field of investigation. Among the few who are prepared at least to give the paranormal a hearing, the subject of reincarnation (the transmigration of souls) is probably the most unpopular. Eastern scientists, by contrast, are much more at home with the idea. This is not solely for religious reasons: the oriental world-view is simply different from the occidental one.

Even so, the evidence in both East and West is discomfitingly favourable towards reincarnation, however much it might upset one's sensibilities. There are countless cases of people who seem to be able to remember past lives. Many of these people 'recall' that they were members of the royal family of Atlantis, and we can with some confidence ignore their 'recollections', since the Atlantean royal family could have been only of a certain size, after all; but others 'remember' lives that were, while not exactly humdrum, at least fairly consistent with the age. And it seems reasonable to assume that people who came to sticky ends might have less difficulty in 'remembering' their previous incarnations than the rest of us. For example, the likelihood of your having been of the French upper classes in a previous life is, in statistical terms, fairly remote – but if you travelled in the tumbril and perished under the guillotine there is a better-than-usual chance that you might 'remember' your former existence – or, at least, the end of it.

The British writer Joan Grant, author of a number of historical novels she claimed were based on her own past-life experiences, accepted this aspect of reincarnation in her

BELOW: *The Temple of Poseidon, Atlantis, as rendered in Sir Gerald Hargreaves' 1954 book Atalanta. Tales of living people who had earlier lives in Atlantis are widely regarded as nonsense.*

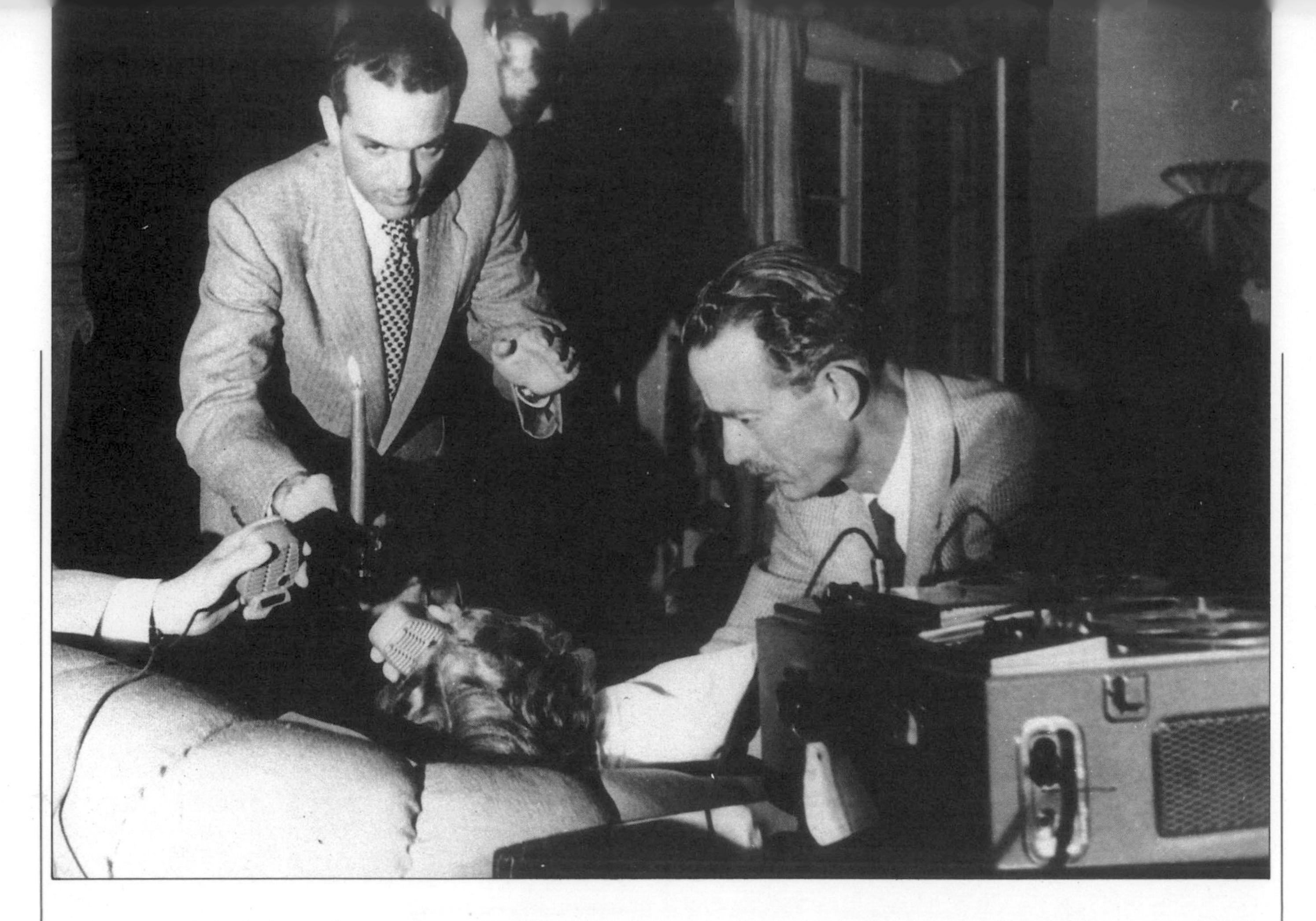

explanation of alcoholism. She suggested that alcoholics in this life had died from thirst in some previous one. Even more plausibly, she drew attention to the times when wounded combatants ended their days in crude military hospitals where the only anaesthetic was cheap rotgut alcohol: if you died, say, at Waterloo, eagerly wondering when your next swig of poteen would come, it is no wonder if in this life you drain every bottle in sight.

Theories like this one are, of course, risible – but only superficially so. It seems far more likely that a powerful emotion could survive transmigration than that detailed memories could, particularly since most of those 'detailed memories' prove on examination to be dubious. One of the most famous recent cases is that of a Colorado woman who, under hypnotic regression, told tales of her earlier life as 'Bridey Murphy', an Irish girl who lived in the early 19th century. The details she recounted of the Ireland of that time were very convincing; yet the whole set of evidence is devalued because, as a child, she had an old Irish nanny. It seems most likely that the tales told as bedtime stories 'implanted' themselves in the child's mind, later emerging under hypnosis.

The same scepticism has to be exercised when thinking of Joan Grant's 'recollections': she seems to have had an astonishingly distinguished set of incarnations, being, *inter alia*, a French princess at the time of the Revolution and that rarest of all things, a female Egyptian pharaoh – one of whose adventures was a trip to Atlantis!

Another novelist who could 'recall' being an Atlantean was Taylor Caldwell. At the age of 12 she produced a book called *The Romance of Atlantis*, purportedly based on her dream-memories of her life as the empress of Atlantis around the time of that continent's demise. The book was not published until 1975 (revised by Jess Stearn). However much one might wish to claim that this was because its contents were a shock to the intellect, the truth is that it contains sufficient inconsistencies and outright howlers to render it poor evidence. In light of the fact that the book was written by a 12-year-old, it seems significant that the name of the Atlantean princess was 'Salustra' and that the man she loved was the Emperor of 'Althrustri'.

ABOVE: *'Ruth Simmons', in reality Virginia Tighe, undergoing regression hypnosis with Morey Bernstein* **ON LEFT:** *In these conditions she seemed to recall an earlier lifetime as a 19th-century Irishwoman, Bridey Murphy. Bernstein's experiments are often cited as proof of the phenomenon of reincarnation, yet there are other possible explanations.* **RIGHT:** *Some years after the 'Bridey Murphy' sessions, Tighe and Bernstein examine a selection of the voluminous mail he received on the subject in the wake of his bestselling and controversial book,* The Search for Bridey Murphy *(1956).* **TOP RIGHT:** *The case of Lurancy Vennum has been widely reported as a good example of reincarnation. In 1877, under hypnosis, she indicated that, in some way, her body contained an additional personality, that of a girl who had died a year or so earlier. The parents of the dead child were convinced, and Lurancy lived with them for a few months until the 'extra' personality departed.*

However, some of the evidence discovered in India during this century has strongly supported reincarnation. Take the case of Sai Baba of Puttaparti, born there in 1926. He claims to be the reincarnation of the great Indian mystic, Sai Baba of Shirdi, who died in 1918. Until the age of 14 he was like any other child, but then he was struck down by a mysterious illness that rendered him delirious for a long period. During this time he would burst into long passages of Vedantic philosophy, speak in tongues, sing songs, recite poetry and so forth. It would be all too easy to dismiss Baba's claims of a previous life were it not for the fact that he seems to be capable of performing miracles.

The classic text on reincarnation is Ian Stevenson's *Twenty Cases Suggestive of Reincarnation* (1966). In his later book, *Cases of the Reincarnation Type*, Stevenson recounted the tale of a child called Jasbir Lal Jat, who died of smallpox at the age of three. Before he was buried, however, Jasbir 'came to life', as it were. A few weeks later he was capable of normal conversation, and now the child claimed to be the son of a Brahmin who lived in Vehedi. Rather unpleasantly, he refused to eat the meals cooked by his mother because he was of higher caste than his parents. Some years later, his village was visited by a Brahmin whom Jasbir immediately claimed to be his aunt. She was initially sceptical, but Jasbir's behaviour on travelling to Vehedi was enough to convince her and others that he truly was a reincarnation of Sobha Ram, a youth who had died of smallpox around the time that Jasbir had himself 'died'.

Evidence from the West is more scanty, but some of it is uncomfortably convincing. One case is that of Lurancy Vennum of Watseka, Illinois, who in 1877, at the age of 13, told her doctor under hypnosis that she was under the protection of an 'angel' called Mary Roff. It proved that there had indeed been a Mary Roff living in the same town; she had died about a year after Lurancy's birth. Mary's parents were confident enough that their daughter's spirit 'lived on' in Lurancy to allow the child to move in with them for three months or so. At the end of this period Lurancy became Lurancy once more, and she rejoined her own family.

It is all very well to cite cases of apparent reincarnation, but this does not help us to answer two significant questions. First, *how* does it happen? Second, *why* does it happen? The Buddhist response to both questions is simply that reincarnation is one part of the cycle of human life: it happens because it happens, and that is the way the universe works. Another possibility quoted is that there are, as it were, only so many souls to go around; consequently they have to be 'recycled'. Neither of these explanations is particularly pleasing. A third possibility is that we, on earth, are merely small parts of the lives of cosmic beings, who choose to 'reside' for a while in human form; bearing in mind the misery of the average human life, this seems implausible (not to mention all the other reasons why it seems implausible!).

There is no viable rationale for reincarnation, and no perceivable mechanism, and so there is little reason to believe that it actually occurs – except that the evidence in its favour is so strong and refuses to go away.

PSYCHOKINESIS

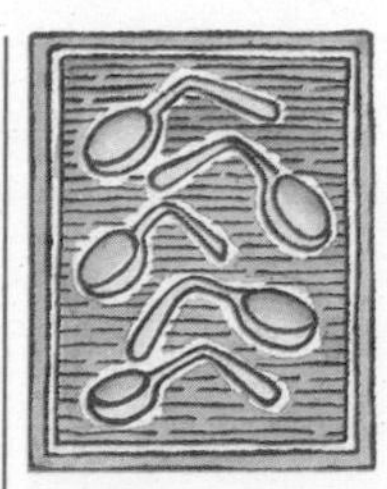

ONE DAY, A BOY Uri Geller, received an electric shock from his mother's sewing-machine. The rest, as they say, is history – or possibly so. It is infernally hard to determine whether Geller is a complete sham, a person genuinely able to mould objects through mental effort alone, or a mixture of the two. Certainly most of his metal-bending effects can be achieved by a competent conjurer, as James 'The Amazing' Randi has demonstrated all over the world. Equally certainly, a good number of paranormally able people have traced the emergence of their powers to some kind of sudden physical or emotional trauma.

Psychokinesis – often called 'telekinesis' – is the ability to move objects through the use of the mind, and it obeys the general rule we have noticed about the paranormal: the more offensive to common sense a particular phenomenon is, the better is the evidence for it. Geller's spoon-bending is a case in point. In fact, it takes only a little skill to make people – even television cameras – believe that you are bending a rod of metal simply by stroking it; but a spoon is a different matter. Professional conjurers such as James Randi have little trouble in doing the trick, but this hardly explains how, after a 1973 television appearance by Geller, children all over Great Britain apparently became able paranormally to wreck the contents of their parents' cutlery drawer.

John Taylor, Professor of Mathematics at King's College, London, performed some fairly rigorous experiments on a number of such children, and became convinced that indeed they were not cheating. Later he was to 'recant', saying that the paranormal was all bunk; yet he was never satisfactorily to explain why it was that children appeared to be able to bend cutlery sealed, for example, in airtight glass containers.

The classic object to move is one's own body, and indeed there are widespread reports of levitation by various gurus and their acolytes. It is hard to know how to evaluate these. One fan of transcendental meditation who went on a course which claimed to teach people to levitate was later heard having the following conversation with a friend:

Friend: And did you actually *fly?*
Fan: Well . . . almost.

However, levitation cannot be dismissed out of hand. The 19th-century British medium, Daniel Dunglas Home, frequently flew, unless we are to discount the evidence of numerous perfectly sober and respectable witnesses. Sai Baba has done the same in India during this century (again subject to the same *caveat*).

Some people believe themselves to be gifted gamblers, in that they reckon they can predict the way the dice or the cards

OPPOSITE: *Sai Baba, to whom psychokinesis seems merely a matter of child's play* **LEFT:** *The Swiss metal-bender Silvio Meyer* **ON LEFT** *undergoing some scientific testing.* **TOP:** *Professor John Taylor examines some deformed cutlery.*

ABOVE: *It is hard to deny the evidence presented by a photograph such as this one – which seems almost certainly not to be a fake. W E Cox claims to have an 'entity' friend, who is here writing a message to him. Current models of psychokinesis would suggest that the 'entity' is in fact Cox's right-brain – but, of course, these are all just theories.* **ABOVE CENTRE:** *A message from Cox's 'entity' friend.* **ABOVE RIGHT:** *Three frames from a cine film of the same series of experiments. showing an aluminium bar emerging through the front glass of the mini-lab.*

UPPER LEFT: *Researcher W E Cox demonstrates an inflated balloon in a sealed box. This might seem rather uninteresting until one learns that the balloon was not inflated when it was placed in the box. And, just to make sure, the neck of the balloon had been sealed using superglue.* **LEFT:** *In an extended series of experiments on psychokinesis carried out in Missouri there were some astonishing results – including this example of a table being levitated.*

LEFT: *The apparent levitation of a table in one of the* SORRAT *psychokinesis experiments carried out in* Missouri. *This photograph was taken on* 31st October 1986. **LOWER LEFT:** *Another* SORRAT *experiment saw* W E Cox *place solid leather rings in a sealed plastic envelope.* On 26th June *these rings were found to have linked; however, soon afterwards they unlinked. Many researchers are less than impressed with such 'evidence'.*

ABOVE: SORRAT *researchers Ray Christ and Joe Mangini under a 80lb (36kg) dining table seemingly levitated to the ceiling before crashing to the floor. This* SORRAT *experiment took place in* June 1966. **LEFT:** *The levitation of a doll during the* SORRAT *experiments.*

will fall. However, when J B Rhine was investigating this subject he discovered that, astonishingly, better results were obtained from people who claimed to be able to *control* the fall of the cards or dice, not merely predict them. Of course, Rhine's experimental techniques were not so rigorous as they could have been; still, one is left with the impression that his evidence for psychokinesis is a lot better than his evidence for, say, precognition. Subsequent experimenters have had similar results.

It would seem that psychokinesis, if indeed it is a genuine phenomenon, is merely a sort of subdivision of poltergeist activity, the topic at which we shall be looking next. Yes, there are people who display the most remarkable psychokinetic powers – Nina Kulagina of the Soviet Union springs to mind – but none of them can compare with the psychokinetic abilities of the average 13-year-old, assuming that he or (more usually) she is placed in a situation that is emotionally stressful.

Psychokinesis is little understood and, like so many paranormal phenomena, is likely to remain so for the foreseeable future: the ability seems to 'melt away' when subjected to rigorous scientific examination. Nevertheless, the ability of certain people mentally to manipulate their environments, even to the extent of making themselves 'fly', has been recorded so often that it is hard to consign all of the evidence to the dustbin.

A related phenomenon is psychic surgery.

Television cameras have recorded a number of instances, notably in South America, of self-styled 'surgeons' performing complex operations on people with no anaesthetics and with no more sophisticated apparatus than a penknife – sometimes without knives at all, simply pulling the tissues apart. The patients have remained conscious throughout the proceedings, and on some occasions have shown an active interest in their own

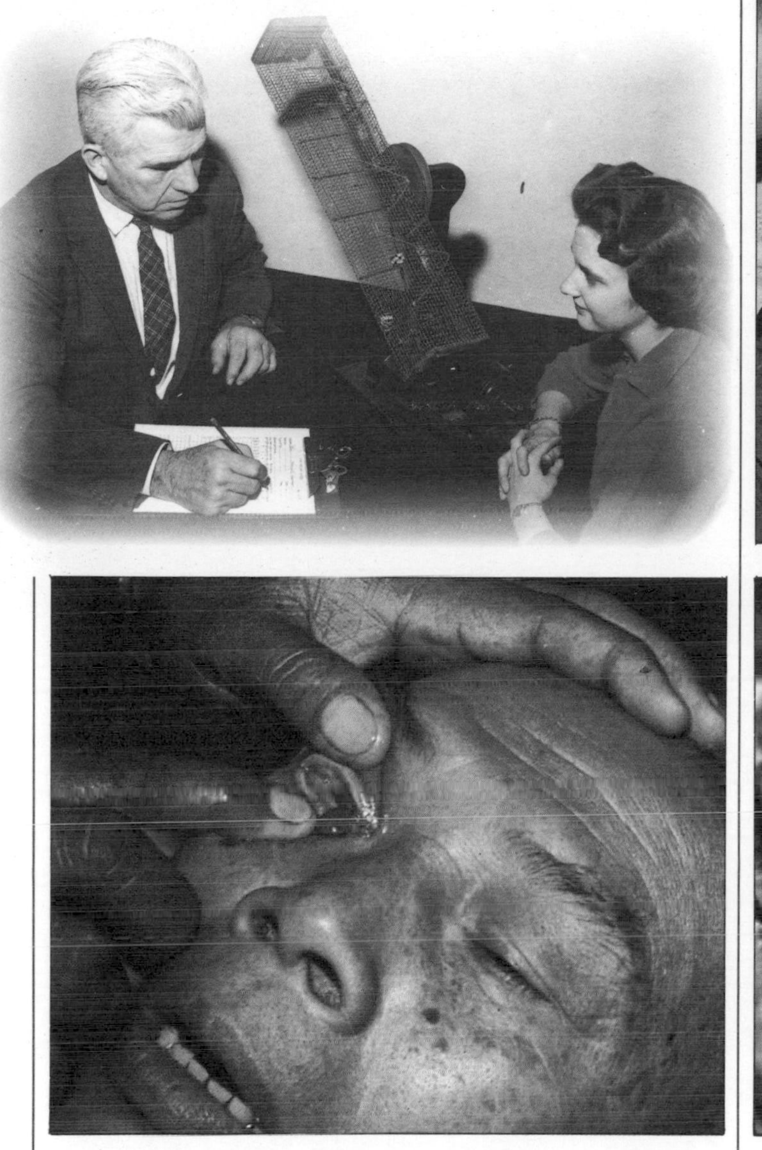

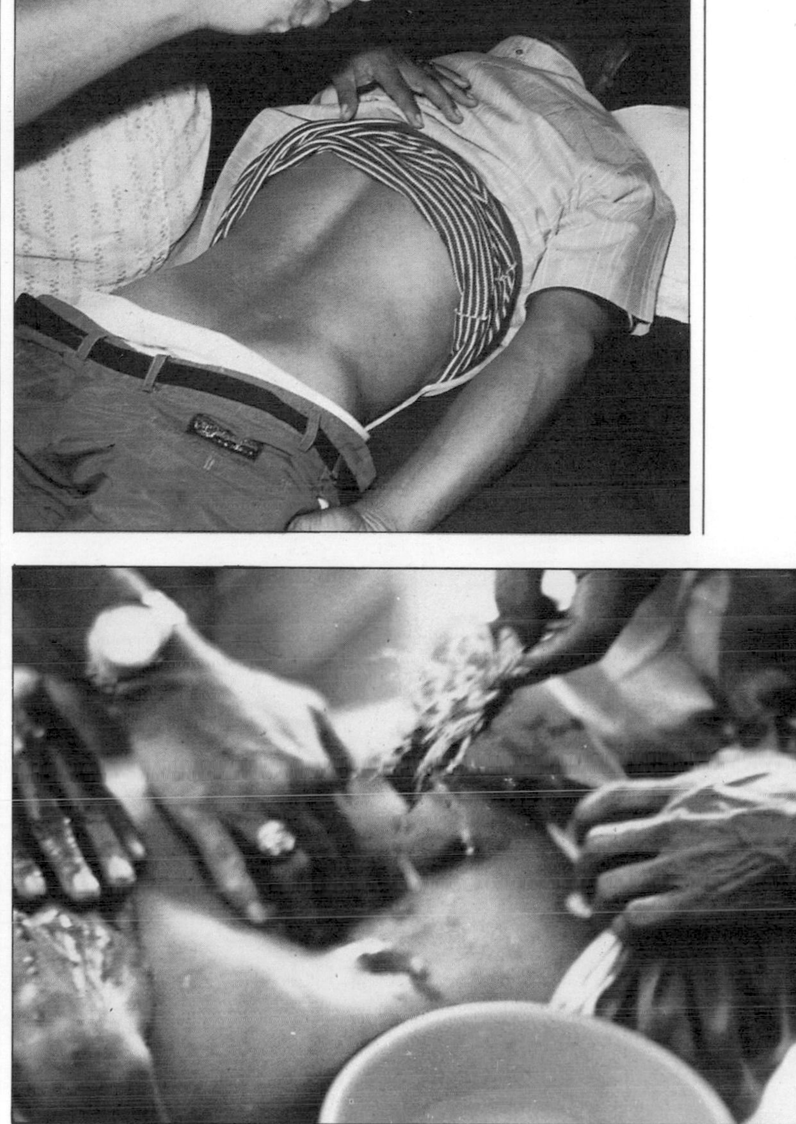

OPPOSITE: *The researcher J G Pratt conducting an experiment on psychokinesis using a dice-tumbling machine. Since the subject was not in physical contact with the dice, there was no apparent way in which she could influence the way in which they fell. Tests like this one have produced much better scientific evidence in favour of psychokinesis than has ever been adduced in the case of, say, telepathy, yet people are more prepared to believe in telepathy than in psychokinesis.* **THIS PAGE:** *Photographs of psychic surgery in action are usually the stuff of nightmares rather than of dreams! That psychic surgery is practised is an undisputed fact, yet modern science has no explanation whatsoever to explain why this can be so. Many paranormal researchers regard it as a manifestation of the psychokinetic ability.*

revealed intestines (one reason for doubting the camera records; most people exposed to their own innards pass out rather than look intrigued). Assuming psychic surgery is not some grand hoax, and there is little reason to believe that it is so, then some kind of psychokinetic phenomenon must be at work.

The rational, occidental left-brain consciousness has a great deal of difficulty in taking psychokinesis on board. Yet the acknowledgement of psychokinesis makes many other aspects of the paranormal so much easier to understand. Of nothing is this more true than the 'poltergeist effect'.

RIGHT: *The classic print of the 19th-century British medium Daniel Dunglas Home levitating in front of witnesses – the party trick to end all party tricks. No one has yet been able to produce any rationalist explanation for Home's feats, and it is impossible to believe that the witnesses were all simply lying: that would have been a conspiracy on too grand a scale. Thanks to Home, tales of levitation became all the rage in the 1860s. This 1863 Punch cartoon* **ABOVE** *satirizes the effect of such tales on high society.* **FAR LEFT:** *A sketch of levitation from Glanvill's Saducismus Triumphatus, 1681. The 'evidence' of such drawings is not held in high regard by researchers into the paranormal.* **LEFT:** Daniel Dunglas Home.

POLTERGEISTS

TOWARDS THE END OF 1965 a house in the state of São Paulo, Brazil, became infested by a poltergeist. A near neighbour, João Volpe, who had studied the psychic, took an interest, and soon determined that the 'focus' of the poltergeist was an 11-year-old child called Maria José Ferreira, who slept in the servants' quarters. Volpe believed the girl to be a natural spirit medium and, in fact, the cause of all the poltergeist activity – although quite without any deliberate intent. He took Maria into his own home for study, a decision his family may have resented, because soon stones were appearing from nowhere to fly around the rooms. This was no joke, since not all of the stones were pebbles: Volpe weighed one at 8lb (4.7kg). Eggs, vegetables and other items filled the air. Maria herself derived some slight benefit from all this frenzied activity; she was able to ask for goodies from the 'spirits' and immediately they would appear at her feet.

So far the 'spirits', although a considerable nuisance, displayed no malice, but then things changed radically. Maria's face and bottom were repeatedly slapped, and needles would abruptly appear implanted in her foot, even when she was fully shod: one time, 55 of these needles had to be extracted. Worse happened: Maria was at school when her clothes suddenly burst into flames, and on the same day the Volpes' bedroom did likewise.

Volpe took her to a well-respected spirit medium, and a 'spirit' came through from the 'other side' to claim responsibility for all this terror, saying that the child had been a witch in a former lifetime, and that now the spirits of those who had suffered or died because of her activities were exacting their revenge. Volpe used spiritualist techniques to ameliorate the worst horrors of the poltergeist, but nevertheless vegetables were still likely to fly through the air when Maria was around. At the age of 13 she committed suicide.

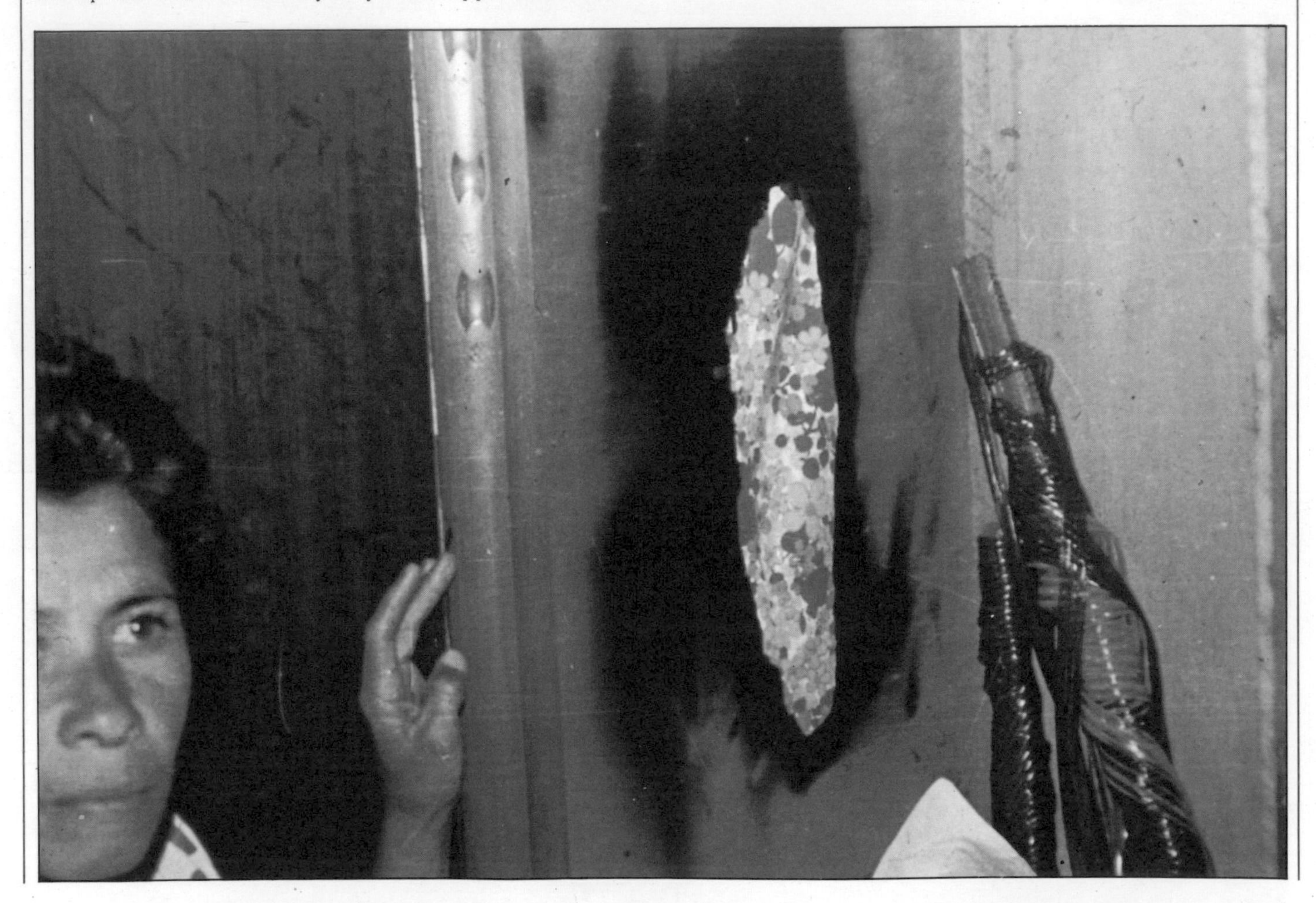

The case of Maria José Ferreira is of interest on several counts. First, it is reported by Guy Lyon Playfair (in his *The Indefinite Boundary*); it is not necessary to agree with Playfair's theories in order to respect him as a meticulous researcher. It is, of course, possible that the wool was pulled over his eyes, but it seems unlikely – although one has to add that he had no direct experience of this case. (He later did directly experience the activities of the poltergeist active in Enfield, England, between 1977 and 1979.) A second point of interest is that the poltergeist became actively malicious, which is by no means always the case with poltergeists. Indeed, poltergeist activity is usually characterized by the fact that, though it is a terrible nuisance, no one is physically harmed. When there is violence in a poltergeist case, it is usually described as one of 'demonic possession.'

The word 'poltergeist' means, literally, 'rattling ghost', and from pre-Christian times until our own it has indeed been assumed that a poltergeist is exactly that, a disembodied spirit which, for reasons hard to understand, wishes to communicate with mortals by making noises or throwing things around. The borderline between poltergeist activity and 'demonic possession' is a hazy one. The latter term is born from two assumptions: first, that poltergeist activities are indeed the product of capricious or malevolent spirits; and second that people would not wish themselves any physical harm. The second assumption is hard to justify: if some people can consciously be masochists there is no reason why other people cannot be unconsciously so. The first is more controversial. The evidence in favour of ghosts is not especially good. That there might be not only ghosts, but ghosts capable of throwing items of household furniture around, seems extremely improbable.

LEFT: *A typical example of the type of damage which poltergeists are capable of inflicting on their surroundings. This particular photograph was taken in Suzano, Brazil, in 1970. Two examples of poltergeist activity in Britain. In South Bromley* **ABOVE:** *around 1973, a poltergeist saw fit to pierce an investigator's scarf with a pin – perhaps a warning that next time it could be the investigator rather than the scarf? In fact, while poltergeists may terrorize human beings, it is very rare that they cause them any physical harm.* **TOP:** *One of the evidences from the famous case of the Enfield poltergeist, investigated during 1977-9 by Guy Lion Playfair and others. Despite the fact that they had been left in a closed drawer, these notes were singed by the poltergeist.* **TOP RIGHT:** *Evidence of fiery poltergeist activity in a 1970s São Paulo case.*

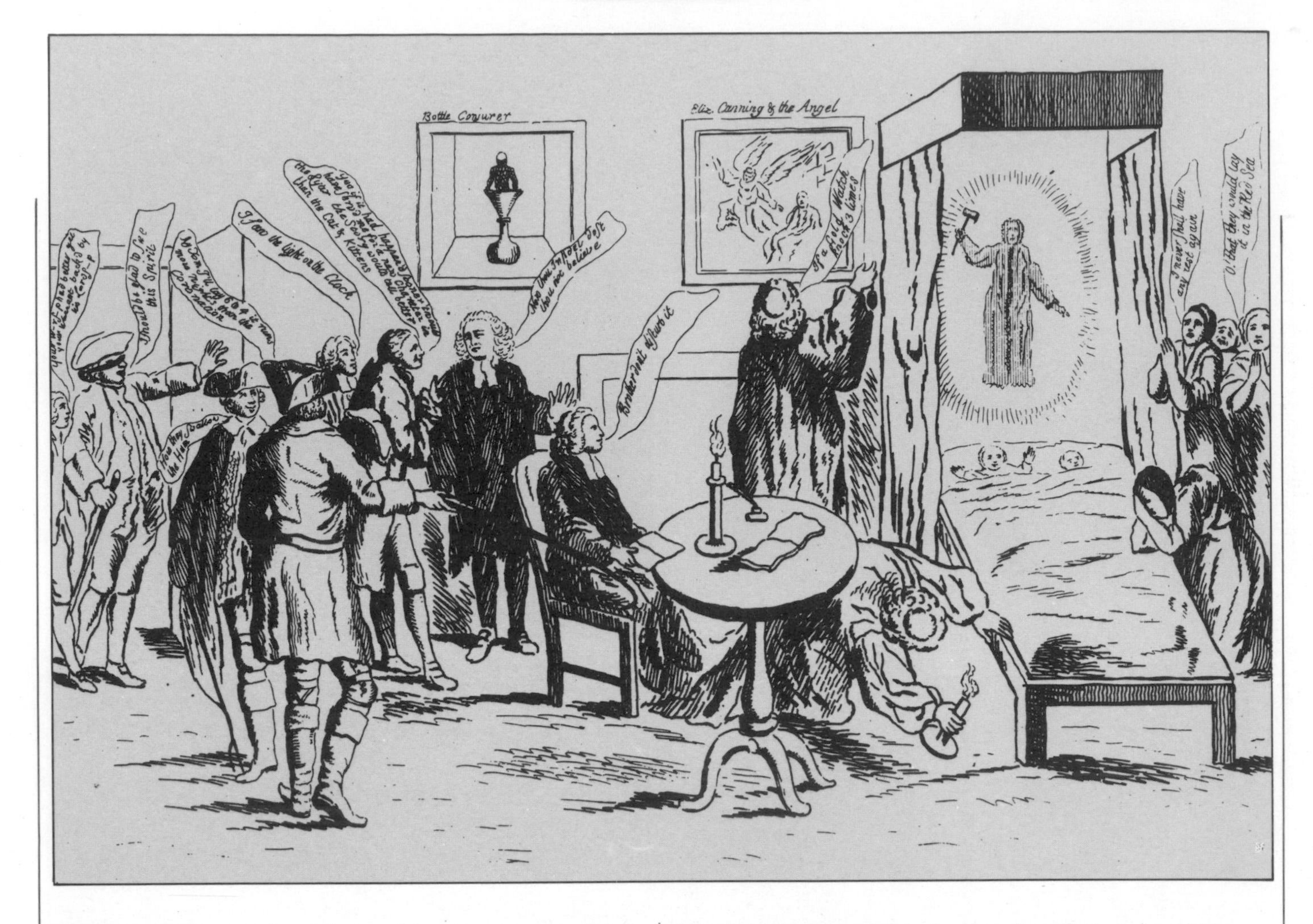

It is generally accepted that poltergeists are *the* classic paranormal phenomenon: explain poltergeist activity and so much else of the paranormal becomes explicable. One of the notable things about cases of poltergeist activity is that there is always a 'focus', typically a pubertal child (almost always a girl). Puberty is a time when the human individual experiences considerable physical and mental changes; few of us ever forget the traumas of our own puberty. It therefore seems reasonable to suggest that poltergeist activity is some sort of product of the disturbed right-brain, which is, as it were, manifesting the fact that it disagrees fundamentally with the left-brain. This idea conforms with the evidence that the usual focus of a poltergeist is a prepubertal girl, whose body's hormonal balance is in a state of flux, preparing for the onset of menstruation.

One of the most famous cases of poltergeist activity is that of the Cock Lane 'ghost' of 1759. It was investigated by a dazzling selection of 'famous names' – Samuel Johnson, David Garrick and Horace Walpole, to name but a few. The situation was complicated. Richard Parsons had taken in as lodgers at his home in Cock Lane, London, William Kent and Fanny Lynes, assuming that they were man and wife. In fact, Kent was the widower of Fanny's sister, Elizabeth, who had died in childbirth; the law stopped Fanny from marrying him, but the two were in love, and so their only option was to 'live in sin'. Not long after the couple had moved in, Parsons borrowed 12 guineas from Kent – a useful loan, since Parsons had not only a family but a drink problem to finance. The repayments of this loan were not properly kept up. Fanny was pregnant. Finally, when Kent was away from home, Fanny requested that the Parsons' older daughter, Elizabeth, sleep with her as company during the long and scary nights.

After Elizabeth had slept several nights with Fanny, Fanny began to complain that their sleep was being disturbed by loud noises. At first it was assumed that this was merely the shoemaker in the house next door working late, but this explanation soon fell by the wayside. Although no one could come up with a reason, the house had clearly become infested by a 'rattling ghost', especially at nights, when the home was filled with the sound of inexplicable knockings.

Shortly afterwards, the pregnant Fanny believed she was in labour, and a doctor was called in. In fact, it proved that she was suffering from smallpox, and she died soon after. Two years later, in 1761, having moved away, Kent married again. However, the knockings still continued at the Parsons' home, despite clergy being called in to exorcise the 'spirit'. The various people involved in the investigation

LEFT: *A cartoon from 1762 lampoons the social luminaries who investigated the Cock Lane Ghost. A surprising number of 'household names' interested themselves in this case: William Hogarth, Horace Walpole, David Garrick, Samuel Foote, Charles Churchill, John Wesley and, last but far from least, a certain Dr Johnson,* **ABOVE:** *During late 1977 a seemingly normal home in Enfield, England, was tormented by a poltergeist. The Harper children – Rose, Janet, Pete and Jimmy – seemed to tolerate the invasion of both the 'rattling ghost' and the psychic researchers with considerable equanimity.*

soon learned how to 'communicate with the ghost' by a system of knocking. The 'ghost' claimed to be Fanny's spirit, and said that she had been poisoned by William Kent and sought justice. This was obviously highly embarrassing for Kent, who attended at least one séance to hear the verdict of his dead lover. The case began to attract considerable popular attention, and finally Kent had had enough. He took the principals to court: Parsons was sentenced to two years in prison, his wife to one, and various other people involved to shorter terms.

The reason for the prison sentences was that it was believed by the court that the knockings had been deliberately caused by young Elizabeth Parsons, and certainly this could have been the case; much later, in the 1840s, the sisters Margaret, Leah and Kate Fox perpetrated a similar hoax, which had as its by-product the creation of the modern Spiritualist movement. It is plausible to suggest that Elizabeth Parsons had a 'crush' on Fanny, and that after the older woman's death she blamed Kent for having destroyed her idol. If her resentment were conscious, then it is likely that the Cock Lane 'ghost' was a fraud; if, however, it were unconscious, then it is quite likely that the case was genuinely one of poltergeist activity. The latter explanation is by far the more tempting, for Elizabeth was at exactly the right age to be a poltergeist's 'focus'.

What, then, *is* a poltergeist? Playfair believes that poltergeists are, as it were, loose balls of spirit energy which delight in tormenting human beings to a greater or lesser degree Colin Wilson, who was one of the first to propose that poltergeists are, like so many other paranormal phenomena, products of the little-understood activities of the right-brain, more recently, after discussion with Playfair, changed his opinions and opted for the loose-spirit explanation. Jenny Randles, best known for her investigations of UFOs, has suggested that both poltergeists and UFOs represent some sort of psychic projection, and that the two phenomena have similar causes or are possibly merely different manifestations of the same phenomenon.

Randles is probably correct, and poltergeists, like UFOs, are probably products of the right-brain. Of course, such an explanation does not on its own help us very much, since it tells us nothing about the real mechanism of poltergeist activity – about how the right-brain is capable of producing such effects. Nevertheless, there are strong correlations between extended UFO cases and extended poltergeist cases. Usually a 'focus' can be found who is a child facing the onset of puberty, although sometimes the individual is older, but similarly enduring some kind of hormonal turmoil. In UFO cases it is tempting to say simply that mentally disturbed people will think they see curious things; but this explanation falls apart in instances where large numbers of people see the same UFO, or indeed when independent observers can, whether they like it or not, experience the influence of a poltergeist. Both types of phenomenon would seem to represent the physical reification of some impulse born of the unconscious (i.e., right-brain) of the 'focus'. The exact mechanism is a puzzle, but it could well be related to the model put forward earlier.

A final poltergeist case is worth brief mention. In 1878 Esther Cox was living in the house of her brother-in-law, Daniel Teed, in Amherst, Nova Scotia; other residents in this packed homestead included her two sisters (one of whom was married to Teed), her brother, and Teed's adult brother and two small sons. Esther, aged 18, seems clearly to have been at the age where she was fully sexually awakened, yet

TOP LEFT: *A sketch by J W Archer, taken from Charles Mackay's Memoirs of Extraordinary Popular Delusions (1852), showing the interior of the home in Cock Lane where the celebrated poltergeist performed. The knockings were frequently heard in the corner at the rear right.* **RIGHT:** *During 1952 the Glynn family of Runcorn, Britain, were pestered by a poltergeist. The police assumed that there was a human, rather than a paranormal, agency at work, and consistently set traps to catch the assumed culprit; despite their efforts, the poltergeist activities continued. Here we see John Glynn surveying the wreckage of his bedroom.* **UPPER RIGHT:** *Colin Wilson, the best-selling writer. He initially believed that poltergeists were manifestations of the right-brains of adolescents but, after discussions with Guy Lion Playfair, concluded that they were instead malicious bundles of psychic energy.*

as a 'nice' girl could do nothing to satisfy her desires, which she possibly did not even consciously recognize. Matters were not helped when her boyfriend attempted to force her to have sex at gunpoint. He fled Amherst in shame, but over the ensuing weeks and months the Teed household was tormented by poltergeist activities centred on Esther. Various objects caught fire, there were numerous cracks and bangs, and Esther suffered a good deal of physical punishment: she was stabbed by a penknife and a fork, hit over the head by a broom, and so forth. Possibly the most frightening incident occurred when a group of witnesses saw writing spontaneously appear on the wall above her bed: 'Esther, you are mine to kill'.

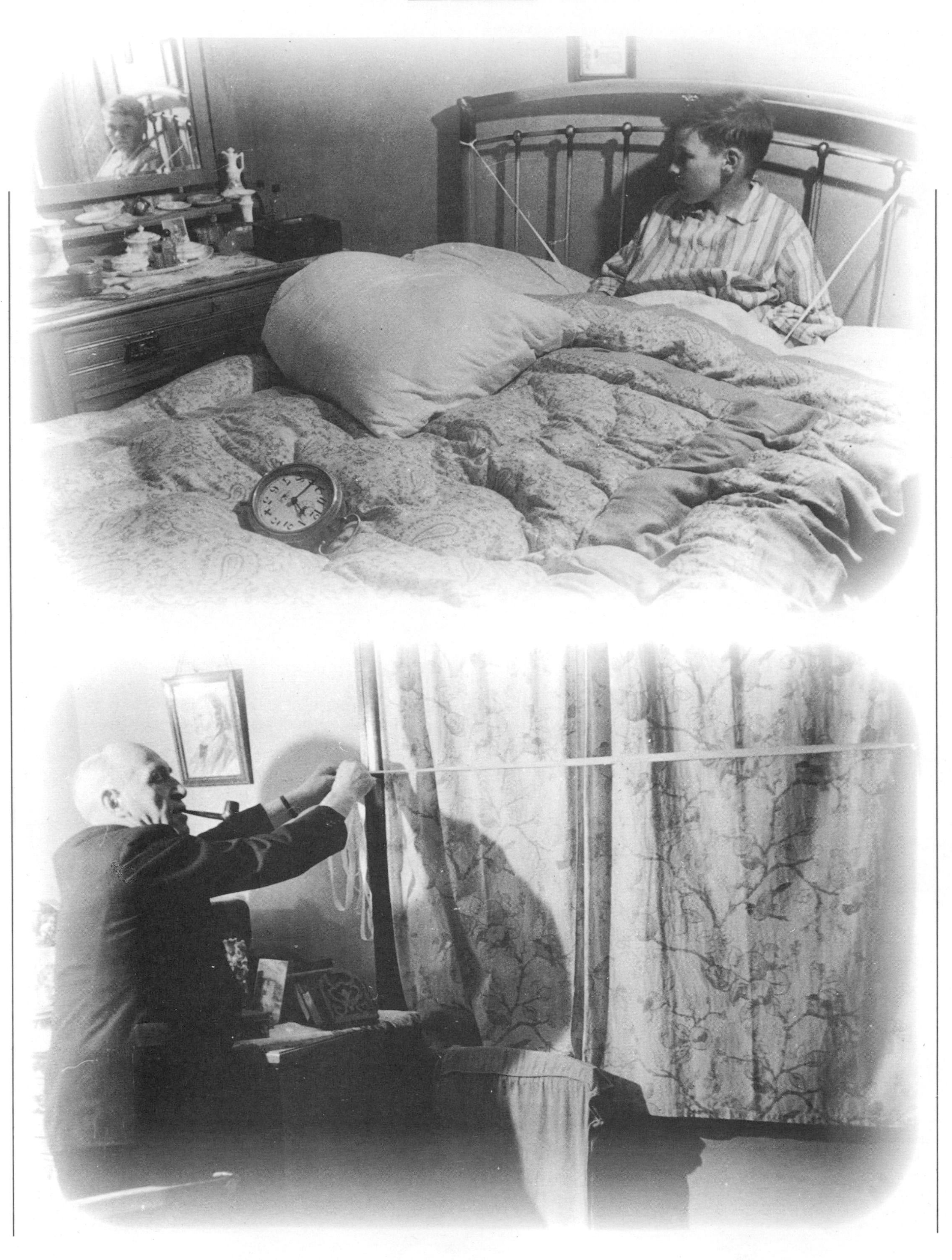

Esther herself blamed the phenomena on spirits who 'spoke to her'. Like Joan of Arc and Peter Sutcliffe, the 'Yorkshire Ripper', she heard 'voices'. In particular, the most malevolent spirit was 'Bob Nickle', a significant name, since the boy who had tried to rape her was called Bob MacNeal. However, it is clear that she was significantly mentally disturbed, and so it is highly likely that 'Bob Nickle' was purely the product of her own right-brain – creating an entity on whom all this mayhem could be blamed.

Some while later Esther was convicted of arson and imprisoned for a few months; the poltergeist activity abruptly ceased.

In an earlier age Esther might well have found herself facing a rather more fearsome sentence than a few months in prison: she could have been tortured or executed for being possessed by the devil. Numerous researchers have pointed up the similarity between cases of poltergeist activity and 'demonic possession'. Some, such as Malachi Martin, have preferred to invoke the influence of Satan, or at least a subsidiary devil. Others, such as Marc Cramer, have suggested that possession is simply a form of mental illness that has yet to be recognized by orthodox science. Both, in their way, may be correct. The torment of the right-brain can quite legitimately be described as a form of mental illness, while its malign activities could well attract the adjective 'demonic'.

LEFT: *The psychic researcher Harry Price was famous in his day, but more recent studies have cast considerable doubt on the validity of his work – indeed, it seems certain that on occasion he simply cheated to create a dramatic effect. The lower picture shows him working on an alleged poltergeist case in Crawley, England, in 1945. In the upper picture we see 12-year-old Alan Rhodes, the supposed focus of the poltergeist,* **ABOVE:** *A sketch by A J Hill of the town of Amherst in 1876.*

AURAS

MANY PSYCHICS CLAIM to be able to see auras surrounding living beings, and to be able to tell from the colour or general circumstances of these auras whether or not the being concerned is in a good state of health.

For a long time this claim was dismissed as just so much psychic nonsense, but then in 1939 Semyon and Valentina Kirlian began a series of experiments in which they took photographs of living objects – from human hands to the leaves of trees – in a powerful electric field. They discovered that around the edges of whichever living object they photographed there was what seemed, to all intents and purposes, to be an aura. Moreover, this aura changed in colour or composition depending upon the circumstances of the person or other entity involved: someone who had just had a swig of liquor would display a brighter and more energetic aura than before.

Photographs taken in this way – nowadays universally known as 'Kirlian photographs' – have appeared in books and magazines the world over. There seems little reason to doubt that indeed living beings do possess auras. However, the nature of these is little understood; likewise, no one knows whether or not the phenomenon has any genuine significance. However, it is worth mentioning a couple of important points. Kirlian auras are not displayed by inorganic objects – such as stones – although they do persist for a while after the death of an organism. Indeed, the classic Kirlian photograph is of a leaf torn from a tree, with part of it ripped away; the aura can be seen following the contours even of the removed section. In both instances it is hard to escape the conclusion that the Kirlian aura is not just some kind of interesting electrical effect, but the genuine representation of a 'life-force' that we all possess and that extends a short distance beyond us.

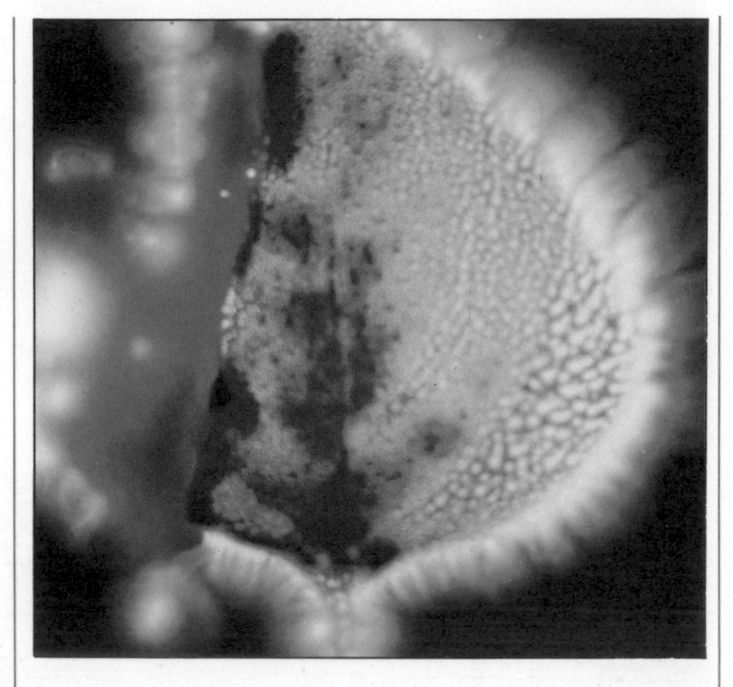

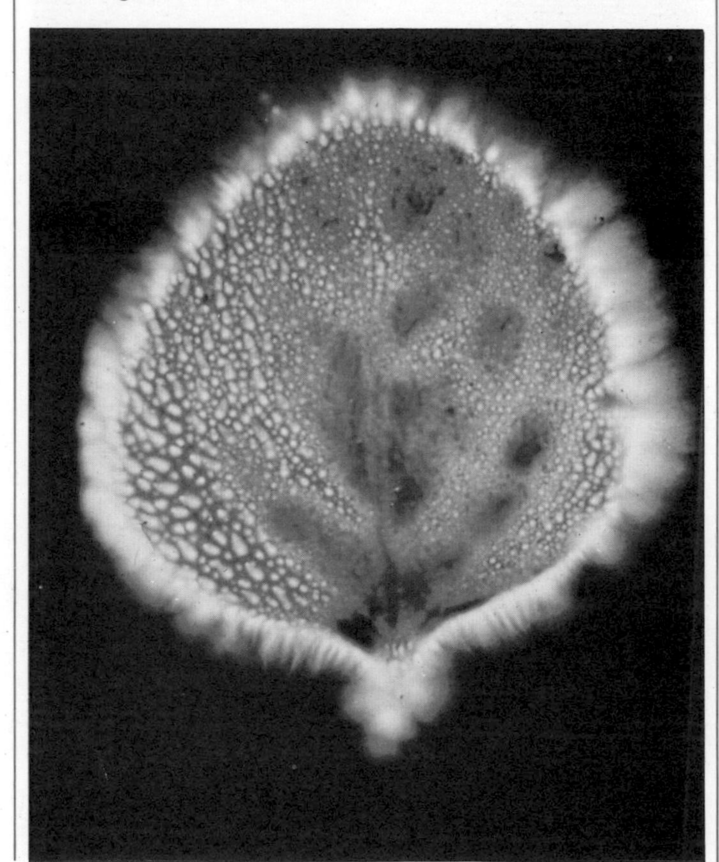

Kirlian photographs of rose leaves. One **LEFT** *is healthy and whole; the other* **ABOVE** *has been cut. The difference in the appearance of the two auras is striking.* **RIGHT:** *The seeming aura around a sea fern.*

OVERLEAF: *Superb examples of abstract art? No: these are Kirlian photographs showing the auras surrounding two human fingertips. It is not difficult to see the difference between the aura of a healthy person* **LEFT** *and that of a drug addict* **RIGHT**.

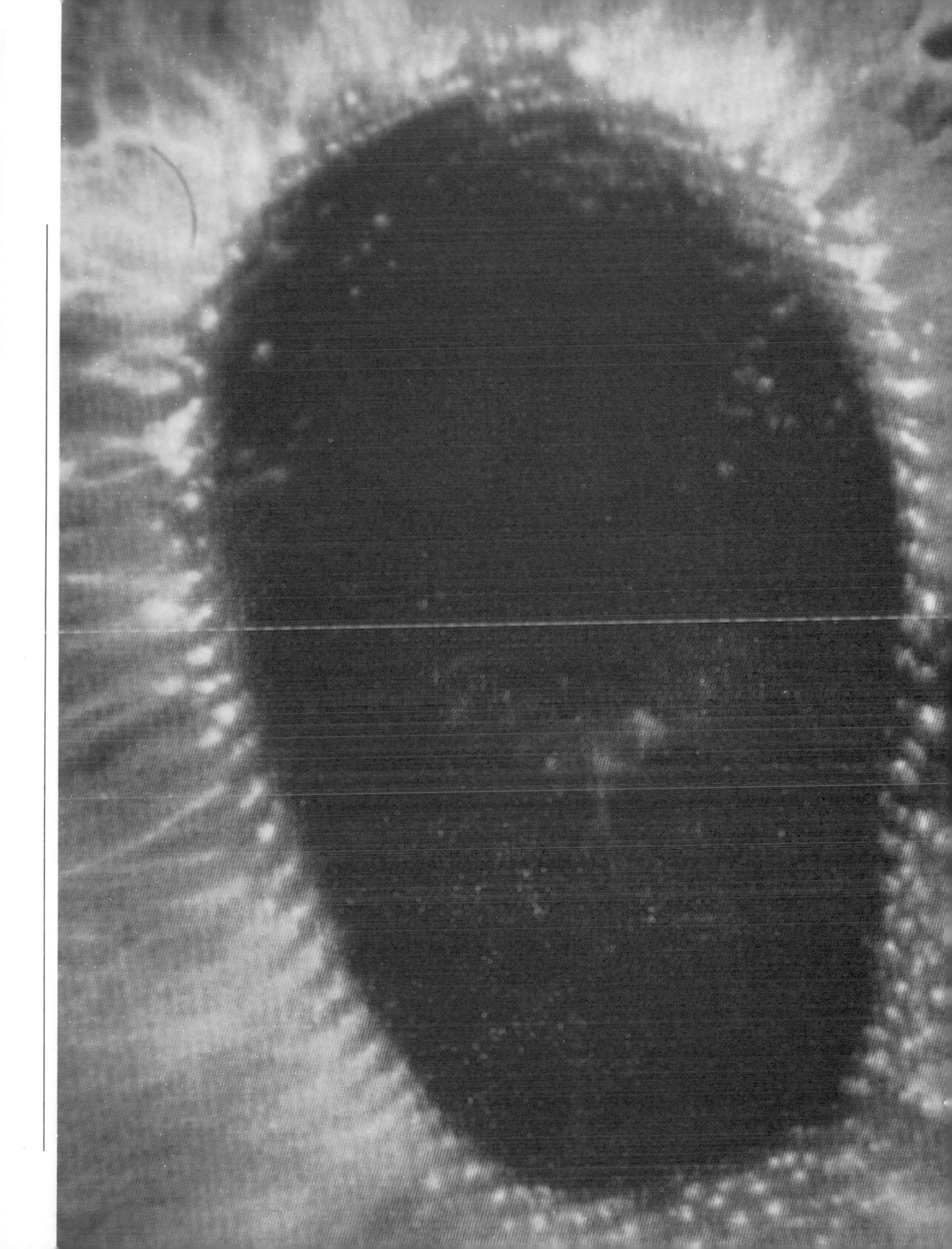

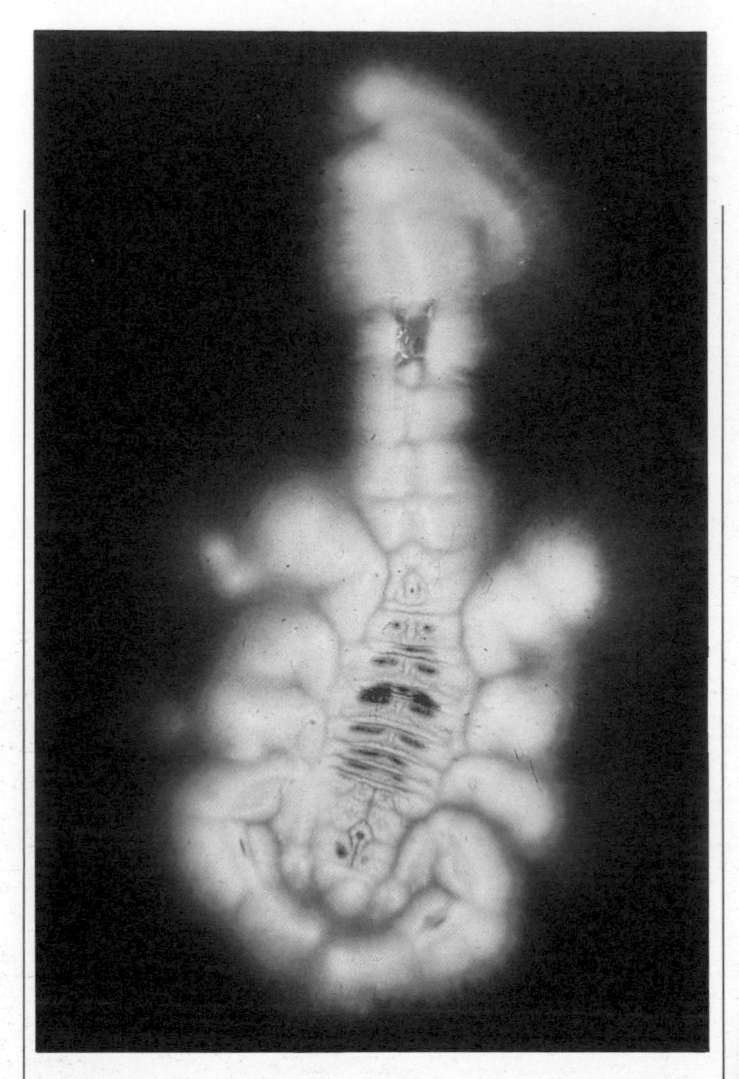

How important is this phenomenon? At one level it may be simply an interesting electrical effect: many of the activities of our cells and nerves involve electricity, and so it is hardly surprising that there should be a detectable electric field surrounding each of us or that it should show changes when we are in poor health. By contrast, believers in vitalism – the idea that living beings contain a certain vital principle absent from non-living objects – claim that the Kirlian aura is the visible manifestation of that vital principle.

The latter notion has led to some of the worst excesses of unorthodox medicine. For example, a 1960s 'therapy' called 'somatography' involved the therapist in massaging, not the patient's body, but his or her aura. Currently popular is 'therapeutic touch', in which the therapist runs the hands over the patient's 'life-field', a few centimetres away from the surface of the body.

Yet the aura must not be dismissed without question. The Christian habit of depicting glowing circles – haloes – over the heads of holy people dates back long before Christ, and is found in many diverse cultures: it is reasonable to maintain that the halo is a representation of the aura. During the 19th century a number of perfectly respectable scientists made studies of the human aura and, interestingly, their results showed a remarkable degree of consistency. To take a single example, Dr Charles Féré wrote in the 1880s of seeing an orange glow around the head and hands of a patient who was suffering from hysteria. He described such glows as 'neuropathic auras', and there seems little reason to disbelieve his reports; he was a professional physician, and had no axe to grind.

Some specialists in the paranormal go further, however. They see the aura as being an 'etheric body', distinct from a person's physical body, and suggest that, for example, OOBEs are really cases of a person's etheric body travelling away from his or her physical body. This explanation is, on the face of it, somewhat foolish, yet perhaps it symbolizes the abilities of the rather 'larger-than-life' right-brain to do things that offend the sensibilities of our rationalist left-brains.

That living beings possess auras is something we can take as almost-proven fact. Exactly what those auras are is another matter altogether.

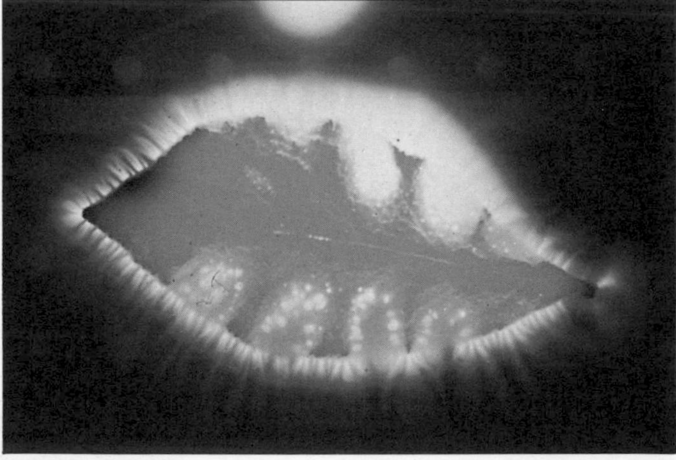

UPPER LEFT: *a Kirlian photograph showing the aura of a living scorpion – much more colourful than the animal itself!* **ABOVE:** *Kirlian photograph of a leaf.* **RIGHT:** *Long before the time of Christ, people regarded as holy were depicted with haloes, which were possibly representations of their auras; this picture, from the late 15th century, shows St Thomas à Becket, murdered in Canterbury Cathedral in 1170. It is possible, however, that the artists who created such pictures were rendering as visible something purely spiritual; we have all encountered genuinely saintly people who possess an 'aura' which we recognize even though we cannot see it.*

aude lux londoniaru
dei prouidentia. na

MAGIC

AUSTIN OSMAN SPARE, WHO died in 1956, was a self-styled magician; he was also a talented artist. On one occasion he was determined to show a visitor that his claims to arcane 'powers' were justified, and said that he would cause rose-petals to fall like snowflakes from the ceiling of his rather seedy lodgings. The spells were performed – and through the ceiling fell the lavatory from the floor above.

Hardly rose-petals! Yet the coincidence was a strange one. Normally things do not descend from the average ceiling, be they rose-petals or lavatories, so the fact that *anything* happened in response to Spare's incantations is perhaps significant. Spare himself thought that his magical powers came from spirits which lived in 'spaces beyond space', as did the bizarre images he captured on paper. More probably, he was tapping the powers of his right-brain, which aided his artistic creativity while at the same time allowing him to perform apparently impossible acts.

Magicians like Spare, Aleister Crowley and others have relied on sexual magic. Their notion has been that, at the moment of orgasm, one can somehow attain, if only temporarily, a higher 'plane', and that this condition allows one to perform various occult deeds. Well, it sounds like a good excuse for having an orgasm.

Yet there may be something in the idea, if only because at the time of orgasm our rationalist left-brains are usually 'switched off'. Perhaps the moments in which our right-brains dominate are indeed times when we can enter a paranormal state.

Whatever the case, the embarrassing thing about various forms of magic is that they appear to work. The anecdote about Spare can be taken as an example of occidental, deliberate magic working – but not very well. Among primitive peoples, who accept such things rather than think about them, magic works very well indeed. Colin Wilson has cited a remarkable case in which a shaman of the South American tribe called the Calawayas believed that his wife was being unfaithful to him. No one could determine the truth or otherwise of his worry, and so it was decided to 'call the condor'. This huge bird is an important part of the Calawayas' world-view: they believe that human beings, on death, are reincarnated as condors. The unfortunate woman was staked out and, sure enough, from the skies a condor appeared: it strutted around for a while, and then made pecking motions towards the woman, an action assumed by the tribe to be evidence of her guilt. A few days later the woman committed suicide.

We have to be careful about what we label 'magic' in this case. The unfortunate wife may have been totally innocent of adultery; she may have killed herself simply because all the rest of the members of the tribe ostracized her, believing in her guilt. It is, therefore, flaunting logic to suggest that the condor somehow 'knew' that she was an adultress. However, the strange part of the whole episode (which was recorded by a visiting television team) was that the condor appeared at all. Condors are not usually enthusiastic about human

ABOVE: *Aleister Crowley, the self-proclaimed Beast 666, in 1929. Crowley is certainly the most famous black magician of the 20th century – at least in the West – yet records of his magical feats are strangely lacking. His doctrine was: 'Do what thou wilt shall be the whole of the Law'. Opinions differed as to his personality; some regarded him as gifted but misled, others as a genius, and yet others as a figure of genuine evil. Today it is difficult to judge, because his system of 'magick' involved a high level of sexual activity – something extremely shocking in the earlier part of this century.* **RIGHT:** *Crowley as a young man.*

company, yet this one swooped from the skies to confront, not just a single human being, but a crowd of eager watchers; furthermore, it did so soon after being 'called'. Possibly this could have been coincidence, but if so the coincidence is an extraordinarily long one, especially since the Calawayas habitually find 'calling the condor' a useful way of sorting out disputes. One feels compelled to conclude that the rituals of the tribal elders did indeed 'call' the bird.

The evidence is overwhelming that primitive magic works, yet we in the developed hemisphere have an astonishingly poor record: people may delude themselves into believing that their magical acts have an effect, yet the results are ambiguous, to say the very least. Aleister Crowley is almost certainly the best-known magician of recent times, but when we look at his record of success we find a total blank. It is likely that magic simply cannot exist among the preconceptions of a technologically advanced society, that a society oriented entirely towards the development of left-brain faculties cannot, by its very nature, spawn people with magical powers. By contrast, a person brought up since infancy to believe that magical events are not only possible but an ordinary part of life is likely to develop paranormal powers. The important point is that, to the person concerned, those powers are in no way unusual; they are simply a fact of life.

RIGHT: *In South Africa potions are made from bark and meat. The witchdoctor will smear the resulting mixture on himself and then administer it to the patient, to pass his power on for the desired cure or change to occur.*
TOP: *'Doc' Shiels, a 'psychic entertainer' and artist famed in his native Cornwall, England, shows how easy it is to levitate people – in this case his daughter.*
ABOVE: *A ceremonial seal designed by J F C Fuller for Aleister Crowley.*

Physical Mysteries

FORTEAN PHENOMENA

THE AMERICAN ECCENTRIC AND writer, Charles Fort (1874-1932), was no respecter of scientific orthodoxies: he 'collected', through his researches in the public libraries of New York, countless curious events which he described as the 'damned' – that is, cases which science rejected out of hand. Typical were newspaper reports of millions of frogs raining from the sky, people disappearing in front of witnesses, and flying saucers. His first two books, *X* and *Y*, remain unpublished; but his later works – *The Book of the Damned, New Lands, Lo!* and *Wild Talents* – created something of a sensation. (His earlier novel, *The Outcast Manufacturers*, failed to set the bookshops on fire.)

Fort presented the 'damned' in a higgledy-piggledy fashion and left it to the reader to decide what was going on. Sometimes, however, he felt moved to theorize. For example, his comment on the debate about whether an object can be accelerated move at a faster-than-light velocity was to question whether it had yet been proved that light actually *had* a velocity. Again, assuming that its craters were volcanic, he calculated that the moon was a mere 11,500 miles (18,500 km) from earth, and only about 100 miles (160 km) in diameter. It never crossed his mind that to explain the tides the average density of the 'mini-Moon' would have to be about ten times of solid lead. A further theory of his was that the earth does not rotate; on this he compromised, saying that it was possible that the earth rotated but, if so, it did so only about once a year.

Fort's theories are, then, the most palpable nonsense. But what about the mysterious events he dug out of the newspaper files in the New York libraries? Some of these have to be discounted out of hand. During the 19th century freelance newspaper-stringers in remote parts of the United States made a good living out of inventing improbable stories which would be featured in the major newspapers, whose editors were unable to check the truth because of the lack of adequate communications systems. Obviously, we do not know which of the stories were straightforward hoaxes and which were true (at least insofar as the reporters perceived them).

However, if only one of the stories collected by Fort was true, we have to re-examine our current understanding of the universe. It is not necessary to agree with Fort's hypothesis that there floats somewhere above the earth an invisible 'island' called Genesistrine, whose frogs, hazel-

nuts, etc., have a habit of leaping lemming-like over the island's edges to shower down upon us. It is, however, necessary to look objectively at the various reports of showers of frogs and hazelnuts – not just at the ones Fort came across in the press, but at the ones produced more recently.

In 1931, a year before Fort's own death, there was founded the Fortean Society (now known as the International Fortean Organization), a body dedicated to investigating the types of phenomenon reported by Fort. The names of the founders

TOP: *A 16th-century view of fishes falling from the sky.* **ABOVE:** *The original jacket of Charles Fort's Lo!, showing a shower of frogs,* **RIGHT:** *Charles Fort was a genius, whatever one might think of his writings, theories and frequent credulity. Here is the man himself, playing on the 'super checkerboard' which he devised.*

do not inspire confidence in the society's objectivity – Theodore Dreiser, John Cowper Powys, Ben Hecht and Alexander Woollcott among them – yet equally it cannot be denied that in the last couple of decades the Fortean Society, through its journal, *Fortean Times,* has exposed quite a number of unusual and unexplained things that orthodox science might rather choose to forget than explore. Indeed, the term 'Fortean phenomena' is now widely used to describe reported events that fly directly in the face of all perceived rationality.

Reports of frogs raining from the air are surprisingly numerous. As recently as 1973 *The Times* reported the showering of a French village, Brignoles, by untold numbers of frogs, and suggested that they had been swept up by a tornado and deposited many miles from home. This explanation seems improbable, since one would expect other elements of the frogs' environment – grass, leaves, etc., – to be swept up and deposited likewise. Earlier in the same year, a golf caddy in Arkansas had reported a similar event. The list of such reports is almost endless, and dates back to well before the time of Christ.

We have to remember that other things do 'incongruously' fall from the sky. It was in 1768 that the great French scientist, Antoine Lavoisier, was called in to investigate reports by peasants in the area of Luce that a huge stone had fallen from nowhere; Lavoisier's conclusion was that the peasants must be lying, because everyone knew that stones do not drop out of the sky. And in 1807 Thomas Jefferson came out with a famous comment: 'I could more easily believe that two Yankee professors would lie than that stones would fall from heaven'. Nowadays we know that stones – meteorites – do indeed fall from heaven, but we are less certain about the veracity of Yankee professors.

Fort was a particular devotee of reported showers of frogs, fishes and the like. However, it would be a mistake to

LEFT: *A woodcut from Expositio Canonis Misse (1496), by Bishop Odo of Cambrai. The scene purports to be the Israelites gathering the manna that has fallen from the heavens. Very Renaissance Israelites.* **ABOVE:** *A 1557 woodcut depicting a rain of crosses claimed to have occurred in 1503.*

assume that Fortean phenomena are all of this type: the range is vast. A notable Fortean phenomenon is spontaneous combustion – in which a person, for no apparent reason, catches fire. To judge by the remains of such unfortunate people, the flames are extremely hot, yet surrounding furnishings show little more than scorch-marks, if even that. For example, in 1966 a meter-reader in Coudersport, Pennsylvania, visited the house of a retired doctor, John Bentley, and discovered that the man had burned away completely except for the lower part of one leg. The flames had been so hot that they had burned a hole through the floor to the basement beneath; yet articles near to the site of the blaze remained virtually unscathed. In a case reported in the *British Medical Journal* in 1891 a

TOP: *Records of so-called 'Fortean phenomena' date back hundreds if not thousands of years before Fort's own lifetime; some regard the Biblical plagues of Egypt as early accounts of such phenomena. This print shows a rain of blood which, it is claimed, fell on France's Provence in July 1608.* **RIGHT:** *Another illustration from Olaus Magnus's* Historia de Gentibus Septentrionalibus *(1555). Clearly the author was enthused by showers of fishes.*

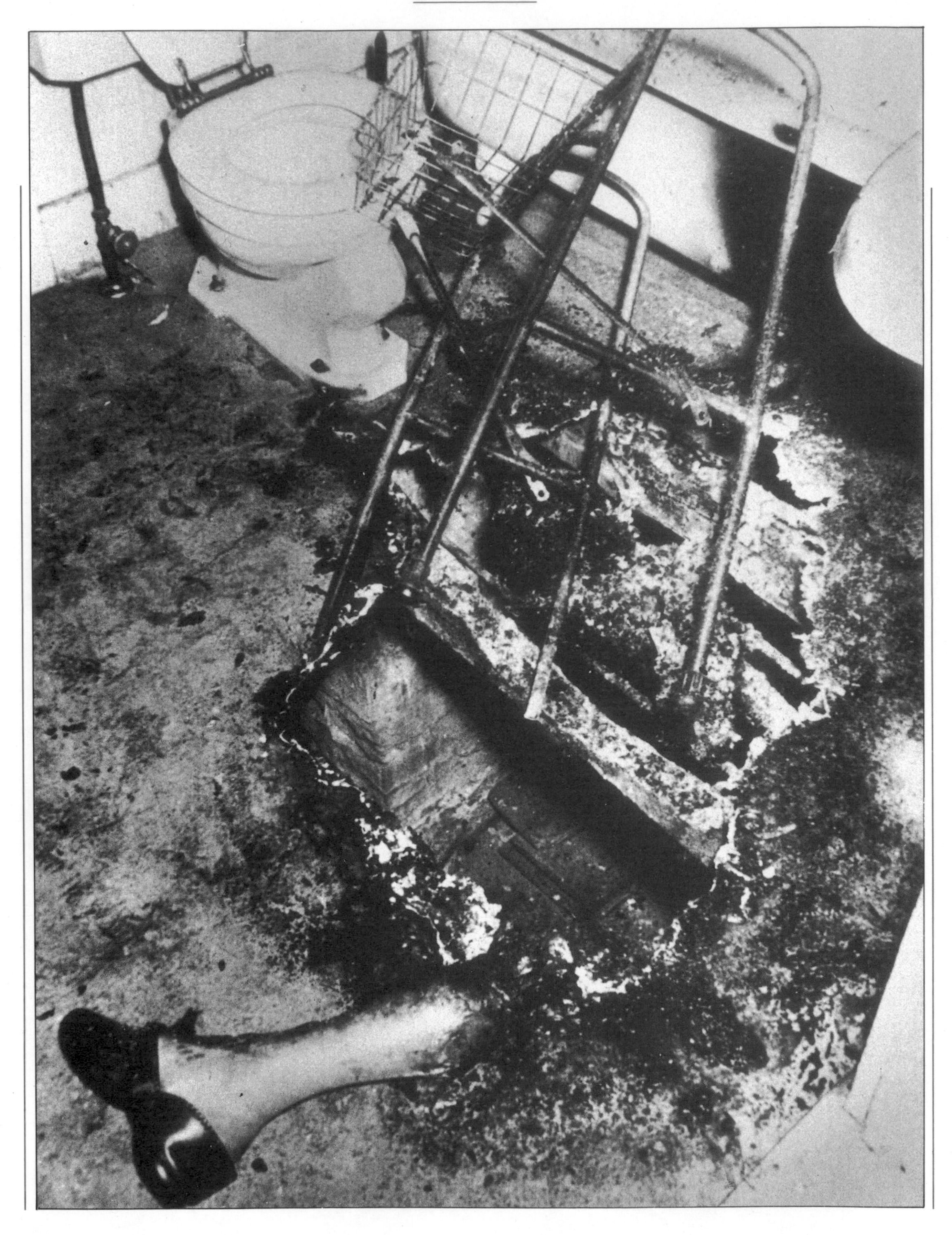

woman's legs were burnt to a crisp, yet the stockings she was wearing were unharmed. Fort reported the instance of the writer, J Temple Thurston, who in 1919 was discovered burned from the waist down, but whose clothing showed no trace of the fire. And in 1951 an elderly woman called Mary Reeser was found to have burned to death in a fire of such ferocity that all that remained were fragments; one grisly morsel was her skull, which had shrunk to the size of an orange, exactly the opposite of what normally happens when people burn to death. Once again, the effects of the fire were extremely localized – in this instance to Mrs Reeser and the armchair in which she had been sitting.

As yet, no one has been able to come up with any remotely plausible explanation for such phenomena as spontaneous combustion: a suggestion that ball lightning could be responsible has been flirted with, but generally rejected, and the charge that the victims were all drunkards, the alcohol in whose bloodstreams caught fire as they lit a cigarette, is unsustainable. This lack of any sensible explanation is characteristic of Fortean phenomena. It is possible to put forward theories about many of the physical oddities that have been reported – such as UFOs, which Fort himself recorded, although the term had yet to be coined – but, aside from Fort's own bizarre hypothesis, no one has yet been able even remotely to give any sort of rational explanation for showers of frogs or for people bursting spontaneously into flames. In fact, the problem is even deeper than it might at first appear: not only do we not know *how* these things come to happen, we have not the first idea *why* they should do so. From the point of view of physics, the events simply do not make sense; a religious person might suggest that God moves in mysterious ways, but a shower of frogs seems to have little religious purpose.

However, at this point we are drawn back to our discussion of the poltergeist effect (*see* page 44). There is no real point in throwing articles of furniture around the room, yet that is what poltergeists do. If, as seems most probable, poltergeist activity is the product of the right-brains of

LEFT: *The remains of Dr John Bentley, who died on 5 December 1966 in Pennsylvania, presumably as a result of spontaneous combustion. Notice how the lavatory seat, which was highly combustible, has been totally unaffected.* **ABOVE:** *The great French scientist Antoine Lavoisier refused to believe in meteorites, the 'Fortean phenomenon' of the 18th century. However, the fact that Lavoisier was wrong should not compel us to believe in all accounts of strange falls from the skies.*

people who are undergoing some mental trauma (typically pubescent girls), then is it not possible that the same people could be responsible for showers of frogs? It is widely reported in instances of poltergeist activity that, not only are existing objects thrown around, articles such as stones and needles seem to appear from nowhere. These items are seen not only by the person at the centre of the poltergeist event but also by onlookers.

Such notions are appealing, but in truth we are theorizing in a vacuum. A typical Fortean phenomenon remains just that – Fortean, or, in other words, totally inexplicable. Yet there are some types of event recorded by Fort which can, admittedly with some difficulty, be fitted into a rational framework. Sometimes the explanation is prosaic, as in the *Mary Celeste* mystery (*see* page 74) and sometimes it calls upon the assumed powers of the right-brain; yet in either case there is at least some sort of logic involved.

The same can hardly be said of a shower of frogs!

ABOVE: *In July 1951 Mrs M H Reeser, of St Petersburg, Florida, was a victim of spontaneous combustion. Here workers clear the debris from her home. No one has yet been able to produce a convincing explanation for this phenomenon – neither paranormal researchers nor orthodox scientists – yet it certainly seems to occur. Perhaps, like ball lightning, it will one day be explicable in strictly rationalist terms,* **LEFT:** *An illustration published in the British Medical Journal in 1888 of an old soldier found dead of spontaneous combustion that year in a hayloft in Aberdeenshire, Scotland.* **RIGHT:** *The fall of the stars, as envisaged by Albrecht Dürer.*

VANISHING PEOPLE

IN 1986 A YOUNG South American woman, temporarily living with her aunt near Taunton, England, seemed to disappear without trace. Her family were well off, and generated sufficient media publicity for reported sightings of the girl to come in from all over the British Isles. Family members followed up all these leads, but every time they seemed to be getting close to her the trail fizzled out. Finally, it was discovered that the young woman had run away from home and had been living the whole time in a Spanish convent. A less well off family might never have found her.

As many as 26,000 people disappear every year in the United Kingdom alone. Some are in due course found, having fled their homes for various reasons. Others are simply lost forever, and no explanation is forthcoming. In 1978 a Devon schoolgirl, 13-year-old Genette Tate, was out on her bicycle delivering newspapers in the early morning. When she failed to return a search was mounted: her bicycle was discovered, but she never was – despite a vast and occasionally sensationalist campaign of media publicity mounted by her father. In 1969 a 14-year-old Norfolk girl, April Fabb, likewise disappeared while out cycling; once again, the bicycle was discovered but she was not. In both cases, it seems most probable that the unfortunate girls were abducted and murdered.

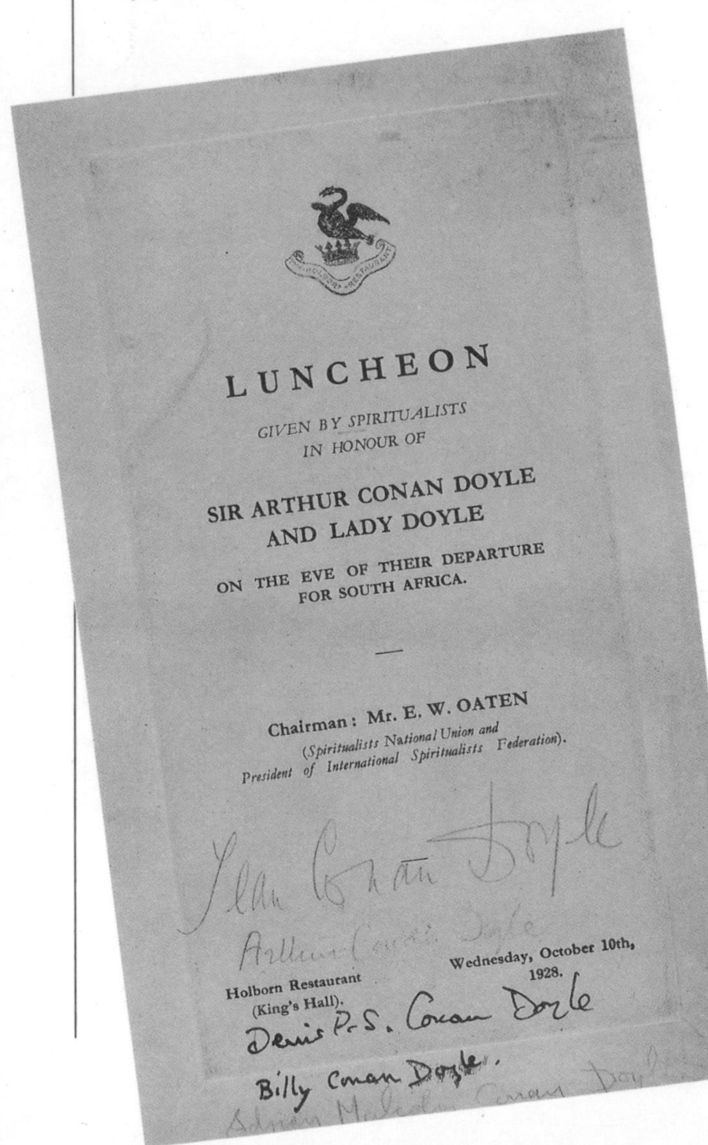

LUNCHEON

GIVEN BY SPIRITUALISTS
IN HONOUR OF

SIR ARTHUR CONAN DOYLE
AND LADY DOYLE

ON THE EVE OF THEIR DEPARTURE
FOR SOUTH AFRICA.

—

Chairman: Mr. E. W. OATEN
(Spiritualists National Union and
President of International Spiritualists Federation).

Holborn Restaurant
(King's Hall).

Wednesday, October 10th,
1928.

Denis P. S. Conan Doyle

Billy Conan Doyle.

RIGHT: *Sir Arthur Conan Doyle is remembered not just as the creator of Sherlock Holmes and Dr Watson but as a researcher into spiritualism; in the photograph shown here the 'spirit of his mother' unexpectedly intruded.* **LEFT:** *Doyle's devotion to matters paranormal can be judged by this luncheon card. Before his death, he promised to communicate from beyond the grave – a promise that has yet to be kept.* **ABOVE:** *Doyle with his wife.*

Yet this may not necessarily be the case, for throughout the ages there have been persistent reports of people disappearing in curious circumstances and for no apparent reason. Many of the most frequently cited instances are in fact merely repetitions of hoaxes produced by 19th-century freelance newspaper-stringers. A certain Joe Mulholland was prime among these 'ornamentors of the truth', and he may have been responsible for the tale of the American farmer, David Lang, who famously disappeared in front of several witnesses in 1880. Later investigation has shown that neither Lang nor his farm near Gallatin, Tennessee, existed; yet the story is still told and retold.

The two classic cases of mysterious disappearances concern the ship *Mary Celeste* and the Bermuda Triangle. The *Mary Celeste* was found drifting in 1872. There was not a single person on board, yet clearly the ship had not been long abandoned – mugs of tea on the galley table were still warm, and the smell of tobacco smoke still lurked in the captain's cabin. Despite sensationalist accounts of the 'mystery', it seems certain that the passengers and crew for some unknown reason abandoned ship. Why else would the lifeboat be missing?

Many of the details of the 'accepted version' of the story can be traced to an anonymous short story published in the *Cornhill Magazine* in 1884. The author was Arthur Conan Doyle, who regarded his fiction, 'J. Habakuk Jephson's Statement', as a piece of harmless fun, and was horrified to discover that items such as the warm mugs of tea were now regarded as factual elements of the *Mary Celeste* story. (Doyle was also responsible for the popular misspelling of the craft's name as *Marie Celeste*.)

So why was the ship abandoned? There are various possible explanations. One is that the crew mutinied, murdered their captain, and then realized that it might be wise to flee the scene. Another, which is rather more probable, is that the people on the *Mary Celeste* and on the *Dei Gratia*, the ship which came across the abandoned hulk, had done a deal in order to claim salvage money. Whatever the case, it seems likely that there are very mundane explanations for the accident.

The myth of the Bermuda Triangle and the people who have 'disappeared' there barely deserves attention. It is a complete farrago. If one correlates the descriptions of various writers, the Triangle extends roughly from the Arctic to the Antarctic and from the Americas to Europe and Africa. The most famous Triangle case is that of Flight 19, a US

training flight which vanished in 'mysterious circumstances'. In fact the documentary evidence indicates quite clearly that all that happened was that the airplanes became completely lost and finally ran out of fuel far from land.

Yet there have been genuine instances of people disappearing. In 1809 Benjamin Bathurst stepped off his carriage at an inn in Perlberg, Germany, to enjoy a short rest, have some food and drink, and go to the toilet. He was seen to walk around to the other side of his horses, checking that they were in fit condition to continue; no one ever saw him again. In 1975 Mr and Mrs Jackson Wright were driving to New York through blinding snow; in the Lincoln Tunnel they agreed to pause and wipe snow from the front and rear windows. Jackson Wright never saw his wife, Martha, again.

In 1873 an English shoemaker called James Burne Worson disappeared into thin air in front of three of his friends between Leamington Spa and Coventry. Or did he? Paul Begg, one of the foremost authorities on cases of disappearing people, took the trouble to seek out the birth, death and marriage certificates of people living in the Leamington Spa area during the relevant period, and found no record of anyone called James Burne Worson. This may

LEFT AND ABOVE: *The most famous case of someone appearing seemingly from nowhere is that of Kaspar Hauser, who arrived in Nuremberg in 1828 with no recollection of his previous existence. Five years later he died in violent circumstances that were as mysterious as his original appearance. Contemporary accounts of him varied; here we see him as both a civilized young man and a woebegone ragamuffin.*

mean that the tale is simply untrue; but there is another possibility, albeit not a very appealing one. Could it be that people vanish not just from this existence but also from the historical records? Clearly, by its very nature, this notion (to which, it should be stressed, Begg does not subscribe) cannot be taken any further, and its possibility is remote.

Of related interest is the phenomenon of 'appearing people', the classic case being that of Kaspar Hauser, a boy who suddenly turned up in Nuremberg in 1828. He could remember very little of his past, but recalled living in a small, confined room and being given only bread and water. The good citizens of Nuremberg adopted him, although there were a number of dissidents. In 1833 he was murdered – or, just possibly, he committed suicide. There is a possibility that the unfortunate Kaspar was the heir to the princedom of Baden, and was treated with gratuitous cruelty by a person keen to improve his or her chances of attaining the throne; however, this seems a trifle unlikely, because a quick murder would have been much more effective and much less likely to be detected.

Unpalatable though it might be, a case can be made for Kaspar Hauser's having in some way 'slipped through' from an alternate universe. Oddly, people are fairly scathing about the notion of alternate universes, despite the fact that they are indicated – although not proven – by modern physics. However, the reports of strange people appearing from nowhere are annoyingly persistent, and other explanations are, to say the least, inadequate. For example, the Englishwoman, Alexandra David-Neel, claimed to have created a person out of nothing (a *tulpa*) during a stay in Tibet; this *tulpa*, born from her deliberate will, was regarded as a real human being by other people, according to her account in *Magic and Mystery in Tibet*. It is hard to believe a word of it – but equally hard to believe she was lying.

There are numerous cases which suggest that people from alternate universes – and hence parallel earths – may somehow find themselves on this particular earth. A couple of examples will suffice. In 1905 a man arrested in Paris was found to speak a totally unknown language: he told the authorities, with obvious linguistic difficulty, that he was a citizen of a city called Lisbian, and rejected suggestions that by this he meant 'Lisbon'. And in 1851 the German authorities picked up Joseph Vorin, who claimed to come from the city of Laxaria in a country called Sakria.

All we can say is that the alternate-universe hypothesis is the least unpalatable of those on offer.

VAMPIRES AND WEREWOLVES

IT IS HARD TO establish quite how many young women were murdered in the early 1600s by the Polish countess, Elizabeth de Bathori, but the figure is generally regarded as lying somewhere between 300 and 650. Her motive for these murders was her desire to perpetuate her own beauty: she believed that bathing in the warm blood of the girls (preferably virgins) would preserve her own youthful appearance. Her methods of murder were, to say the least, unpleasant. She and the servants who had followed her repellent orders were brought to trial in 1611: thanks to our ancestors' customary notions of justice, the servants were burned to death while the countess was merely immured in her castle for the rest of her natural life.

A similar case had occurred nearly 200 years earlier, when the French aristocrat, Gilles de Rais, who had fought heroically against the English alongside Joan of Arc, was found to be responsible for the sadistic rape-murders of 150 or more children. He and his servants typically cut open the children's abdomens, so that he could view their internal organs while they yet lived; often he would sit, sexually aroused, on the stomachs of the children as they went through the final moments of their agonized deaths. Unlike the Countess de Bathori, Rais suffered the death penalty.

Both of these aristocrats – vile murderers or psychopaths, depending upon one's viewpoint – were vampires in that they gloried in the blood of other people. More than that, they actually *required* it. The political system of the day allowed them to perpetrate their crimes for extended periods, despite widespread rumours among the common people. Yet even today vampirism exists. Idi Amin, until 1979 dictator of Uganda, is widely reported to have sucked or eaten the internal organs of some of his murdered political opponents, and there are similar accounts of Haiti's 'Papa Doc', François Duvalier.

The classic vampire of stage and screen is of course Dracula, created in 1897 by Bram Stoker for the famous

horror novel. The reason the book was so successful was probably that Stoker, consciously or unconsciously, managed to put his finger on the undercurrent of eroticism associated with vampirism. This sexual element seems certainly to be present: the Countess de Bathori, although married, was certainly a lesbian deriving erotic pleasure as she bathed in the blood of her young female victims; Gilles de Rais, a rampant homosexual, vastly preferred that his victims be boys, although if necessary he would 'make do' with girls.

ABOVE: *Countess Elizabeth de Bathori, a woman who relied upon the blood of young girls in order – so she thought – to preserve her own youthfulness. The unfortunate girls were savagely tortured to death in order that the last drops of their blood could be extracted. The countess was finally tried for her disgusting crimes, and spent the last few years of her life immured in her castle* **LEFT. RIGHT:** *The letter-heading of* The Dracula Society, *whose founder members include film stars Christopher Lee, Peter Cushing and Vincent Price. The lettering is based on the style used in Romania during the 15th century, at the time of Vlad the Impaler.* **BACKGROUND:** *Gille de Rais' seal for his safe-conduct.*

The prototype of Stoker's fictional Dracula was the real-life, 15th-century Walachian prince, Vlad IV, known as 'Vlad the Impaler', who was a military resistance leader. Curiously, he is in fact even now something of a cultural hero because of his military campaigns, yet he derived his nickname from his habit of dealing with prisoners-of-war by impaling them on sharp poles, reportedly deriving considerable enjoyment from watching them as they writhed helplessly in their death agonies. Whether he was a psychopath or a true vampire is impossible to determine.

Vampirism, from our modern viewpoint, is a psychological condition that is difficult to explain. For most of us, the thought of drinking warm human blood – or even, for that matter, animal blood – is enough to turn the stomach. Linking the experience with any erotic feeling whatsoever is likewise difficult. Yet there are people who find the practice sexually arousing – who *need* the experience.

The vampires of fable are of course rather different. They are not mentally disturbed murderers, but supernatural beings. They are 'living dead' who must sleep by day and venture abroad only by night. They are capable of changing their form from that of a human to that of a bat. They convert other people into vampires by sucking blood directly from their victims' jugular vein.

This image of the vampire is found throughout a surprisingly wide range of epochs and diversity of cultures, which has led many theorists to suggest that such bizarre creatures did in fact exist. However, we can see in the composite characterization a number of basic elements of folk-legends. For example, the ability of people, spirits or other entities to change shape on whim is an idea common to many primitive cultures: in the form of the shape-changing phantom hitch-hiker, it is found even in the popular folklore of Western society. Likewise, the concept of the 'living dead' is found in many parts of the world – think of the zombies of the Caribbean – while tales of blood-sucking people or spirits can be traced back at least as far as the ancient Greeks.

LEFT AND RIGHT: *Nothing, it was believed, could prevent a werewolf having its wicked way with a human being, preferably a nubile female. Although wolves were indeed dangerous predators on human communities a few centuries ago in Central Europe, it is likely that legends about werewolves grew up for tribalistic reasons; a characteristic of tribes is that they are often keen to seek out scapegoats. What better scapegoat than a person accused of being able to turn into a wolf and savagely assault human beings? The bestial executions of so-called werewolves were matched only by those of women condemned as witches.* **ABOVE:** *Gilles de Rais – military hero and sadistic mass-murderer.*

All of these characteristics can be placed in the category of 'elemental fears'; that is, the very idea of them makes the average human being, whatever his or her cultural background, shudder. It is perhaps curious that to vampires has not been attributed the most frequently found 'elemental fear', the possession of feet 'fitted on backwards', a notion discovered in many folklores.

Werewolves – or, to be technical, lycanthropes – share with vampires many characteristics of folklore. They, too, are capable of changing their shape, and of course they use their supernatural strength to overpower and devour their victims. Here it would seem that popular fantasies about vampires have been grafted onto the dread felt for wolves – a dread that was very real, and far from foolish, in medieval Europe. Interestingly, it was widely believed that werewolves, on death, became vampires.

Another belief concerning werewolves was that, in their human form, they had a layer of hair underneath their skin; when they transformed themselves to become wolves, they simply turned their skin inside-out. This belief led to the slaughter of many innocent people, who were ripped open by ignorant mobs who believed they might be werewolves, and who sought proof. As with the contemporaneous witch hunts, which are more familiar to us, innocence did not save the unfortunate suspect from a particularly ghastly death.

It is improbable that there are or ever have been werewolves. But, as we have noted, vampires are still among us in the 20th century. Of course, they cannot get away with their activities on the same scale as did the Countess de Bathori – or perhaps they can. Between about 1910 and 1934 the American sadomasochistic maniac, Albert Fish, killed, raped and partially ate an untold number of children; he was caught only because he wrote a gloating letter to the mother of one of his victims. He confessed to killing some 400 children, although he was so insane by the time of his arrest that it is impossible to judge the validity of this. Over roughly the same period the so-called 'Monster of Düsseldorf', Peter Kürten, murdered and raped nine children, cutting their throats and drinking their blood. In prison awaiting his trial, he too wrote to the parents of some of his victims: the letters do not make enjoyable reading. He said drinking blood was to him as necessary a part of life as alcohol and cigarettes are to others. More recently, in the early 1980s, the London murderer, Dennis Nilsen, killed up to 16 young homosexuals whom he picked up in gay bars; his practice was then to dissect the body, cook it, and often eat parts of it. Reporters who have met Nilsen, a retiring civil servant, all agree that you could hardly meet a nicer man – the same was said of Fish and Kürten.

Clearly there is a relationship between vampirism and sex, and it is hard to escape the conclusion that this is because so many people – usually male – regard the sex act as an expression of dominance: we have phrases in the language such as 'sexual conquest', for example. Vampirism, involving the death and prior or subsequent sexual humiliation of the victim, is, from this viewpoint, the ultimate subjugation of another human being.

A further characteristic that must be noticed is the fundamental cowardice involved in vampiristic acts. As in cases of rape, most of the people we have noted were expressing their power over people who were utterly defenceless. The Countess de Bathori and Gilles de Rais had armies of servants to ensure that their unhappy victims had no chance of escape – and anyway they seem to have believed that their high positions in society would protect them from prosecution. Fish and Kürten preyed upon children. Although Nilsen picked on people his own size, he first of all poured enough alcohol into them to ensure that they had little chance of resisting his onslaught. (Those who did failed to report the event to the police because of fears that, as homosexuals, they might receive rough treatment.)

LEFT: *The belief in werewolves expressed through an early print showing one of the supposed monsters attacking a man. It may have been because wolves are intelligent animals that the idea that some of them were really humans in disguise sprang up.*

RIGHT: *The death of Gilles de Rais was not a pleasant one – yet it was far more merciful than what he had done to 150 or more children. Like Elizabeth de Bathori, de Rais revelled in the taking of blood; like her, he can be classified as a true vampire.*

Are vampires, as has often been suggested, people possessed by evil spirits? Such an explanation is facile, a fobbing-off of responsibilities on to the supernatural. Clearly vampirism is a psychological condition of which we as yet know little, created by social or genetic forces of which we as yet know even less. In general, we can note that vampires have suffered an 'over-parented' childhood – either they have been treated with excessive strictness or they have enjoyed a surfeit of pampering. However, this is almost certainly not the whole explanation.

Fears of the traditional vampire still survive. In 1973 a Polish expatriate, Demetrius Myiciura, was found dead in his flat in Stoke-on-Trent, England. He had choked to death on a clove of garlic which he had put in his mouth last thing at night; on his windowsill was a bowl of urine into which garlic had been mixed; salt had been sprinkled over his bed. Clearly Myiciura had been terrified of nocturnal vampiric attack. His death came about solely because of his terrors. Sadly, all too many children and young women have lost their lives because of the activities of genuine vampires.

LAKE MONSTERS

DURING 1987 AN EXPEDITION searching Loch Ness, Scotland, picked up sonar traces of an object which the expedition members believed to be a fish or marine mammal; it was about the size of a large shark. The researchers dismissed suggestions that it might have been simply a rock, on the good grounds that, when they passed over the same area again later, the object was no longer there. They believed that they had finally come up with good evidence favouring the existence of the Loch Ness Monster – Nessie – although of course they had no means of telling what sort of animal Nessie might be.

There are a number of problems surrounding any claim that a huge creature dwells in the dark, cold waters of Loch Ness. The obvious one is that there cannot be just a single Nessie: there must be a whole extended family of them – in which case, why are sightings so rare? Another difficulty is that various observations of Nessie have differed quite dramatically from one another in their details: surely the loch cannot be populated by so many types of unknown animals!

A popular theory is that Nessie is a surviving plesiosaur, a marine reptile whose heyday, as with the other great reptiles, ended about 65 million years ago. The 1987 report might seem to support this hypothesis, because plesiosaurs looked much like dolphins, and dolphins of course look much like sharks. Yet there are again difficulties with this idea. For one thing, for a long period before about 10,000 years ago, Loch Ness, as a result of the Pleistocene Ice Age, was capped by a vast glacier. It would have been hard for any animal to have survived in the icy waters, even more so in

ice. This objection assumes, of course, that Nessie is not a comparatively recent immigrant: it is perfectly possible that a family of dolphins, whales or sharks accidentally found their way into Loch Ness a few hundred years ago and have dwelled and bred there ever since.

Photographs of Nessie abound, but few prove convincing on analysis. Some are definite fakes; others are not quite fakes, but are obviously not pictures of a monster – a much reprinted example would seem to show a 'monster' at most 20in (50cm) long, to judge by the pattern of the ripples surrounding the emergent head of the creature. (Almost certainly, this particular 'monster' was a water-bird.) Other pictures show logs floating downstream.

ABOVE: *A photograph taken at Loch Ness in 1933 by Hugh Gray is widely believed to show one of the animals thought to be resident in the lake. Gray's initial estimate was that the animal was about 40ft (12m) long, although he later modified this to 'very great'. Assuming that his recollection of its size is reliable, it is rather difficult to think what else this might be except the famous 'monster'.* **LEFT:** *The most famous of all the photographs purporting to show 'Nessie', this was taken in 1934 by the London surgeon R K Wilson. Conventional naturalists have proposed that the animal responsible was either a diving otter or a bird – in either case, a creature far smaller than the 'monster' is reputed to be.*

So, is there a monster in Loch Ness? The scientific evidence is poor, but reports from around the world – notably from North America – suggest that the idea is not so silly as it might seem. Numerous small lakes in Ireland are reported to have monsters; Lough Nahooin is one example. Lake Onegan, in British Columbia, apparently sports a creature called Ogopogo. Bear Lake, in Utah, is said to contain a monster, as is Lake Payette in Idaho. All are inexplicable.

It is possible that there is some connection between reports of lake monsters and sightings of UFOs – assuming that one believes in one of the psychological explanations of UFOs (*see* page 100). In the age when witches were credited with riding around the sky on broomsticks, people quite genuinely saw witches on broomsticks. Whether or not there was any objective reality in what they saw is a matter for debate. Similarly, now that we are all tuned in to the notion of visiting spaceships, people see what look like spaceships. It might well be that exactly the same mechanism is involved in sightings of monsters. Once a legend, for whatever reason, has come into existence, people will believe that they are likely to see monsters in that particular body of water and, purely because of their expectations, will actually do so.

Alternatively, of course, there may well be monsters in Loch Ness.

Jennifer Bruce, *visiting from* Vancouver *in* 1982, *took a photograph of* Urquhart Bay, Loch Ness **ABOVE:** *At the time she noticed nothing unusual, yet a blow-up of the photograph* **ABOVE RIGHT** *reveals a traditional* 'Nessie' *head.* It is *obviously difficult to establish the scale of the creature in this photograph, but the resemblance between it and whatever it was that* R K Wilson *photographed (see page* 83) *is plain.* **LEFT:** *A claimed picture of* Nessie *shot by an anonymous photographer in* September 1983. **RIGHT:** *A model of* Ogopogo *on display at* Kelowna, British Columbia.

AUGUST · 14 · 15 · 16 · 17 ·

BIGFOOT

IN 1970, IN NEPAL, two mountaineers, Don Whillans and Dougal Haston, came across a set of mysterious footprints at an altitude of about 13,000ft (4,000m). That night, Whillans was looking from his tent when he saw, some distance away in the moonlight, what seemed to him to be an ape-like creature moving on all fours. He could not make out any details.

Very few Europeans or North Americans have seen anything that might be the fabled Abominable Snowman, or Yeti, despite the fact that a number of expeditions have been sent from Europe specifically to track the mysterious beast down. A number of Westerners have *claimed* to have seen Yeti but, as John Napier has demonstrated in *Bigfoot*, the standard work on the subject, their accounts can be dismissed as misperceptions (or just plain hoaxes). The same is true of some of the celebrated photographs of animal tracks in the high Himalayas; the tracks can be seen to have been made by langurs, bears or even orangutans.

Yet a few of the photographs cannot be explained away so easily, and there is a powerful tradition among the Sherpas that there does indeed exist some kind of hairy humanlike creature in those mountain fastnesses. On the one hand, folk traditions often contain complete myths; on the other, the Sherpas obviously know a great deal more about the mountains than does any Westerner, and we should not dismiss their evidence out of hand. Moreover, there is corroborative evidence that a species of large, wild humanlike creatures may exist: there are several reports from North America of the Sasquatch, or Bigfoot, which is in many ways very similar to the Yeti. Clearly there is some link, either biologically or in terms of human psychology, between the two.

Here we shall take 'Bigfoot' to be the generic term for wild people, differentiating between the Asian Yeti and the North American Sasquatch. In addition, we have the humanlike Almas of the Soviet Union, Mongolia and China; an intriguing suggestion is that this latter might represent the last surviving relics of Neanderthal Man. Other areas of the world sport their own tales of wild races.

Thanks to the entertainment media, our popular perceptions of Bigfoot are muddled. Children may thrill to the thought that Bigfoot is implacably hostile and murderous, yet many of the traditions say quite the opposite, that Bigfoot is shy and frightened of human beings, which is precisely why it resides only in the most remote parts of the world. Another misconception is that Bigfoot is huge, towering above a human being; again, the various direct-encounter reports, when collated, show that the average height estimated is 5-6 ft (1.5-1.8 m) and sometimes much shorter. One can suggest that in fact Bigfoot is probably somewhat shorter than a normal adult human being, because observers of Bigfoots will almost inevitably exaggerate the dimensions of the 'monsters' they have seen. Both of these aspects would tend to support the hypothesis

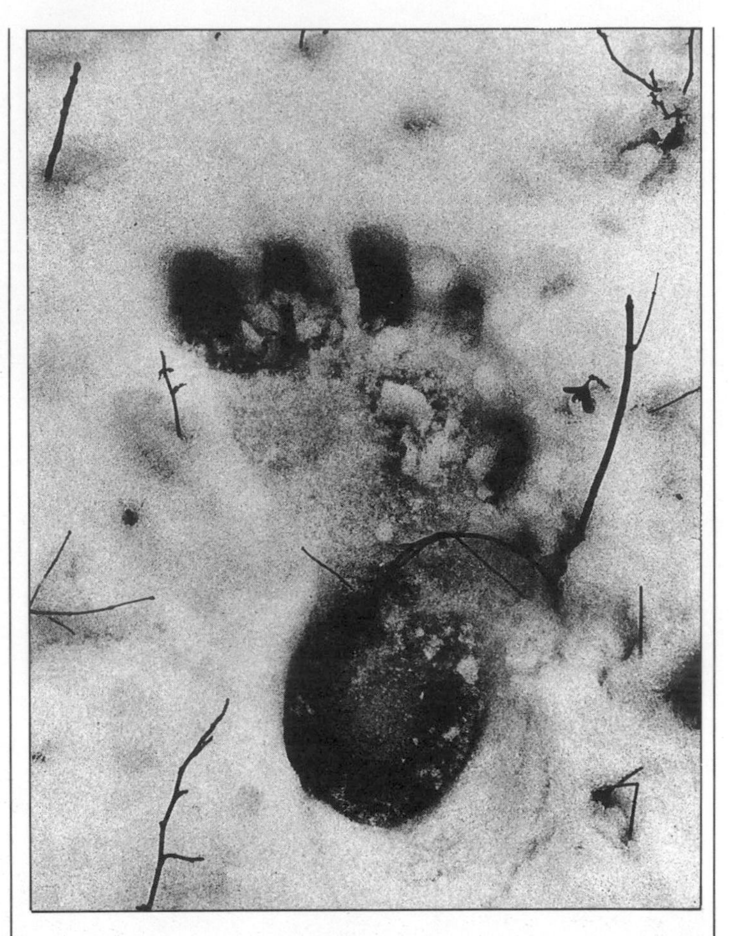

RIGHT: *Paul Freeman, who claims to have seen a Bigfoot on 10 June 1982 in Umatilla National Forest, near Walla Walla, Washington State. In his right hand he holds a plastercast of the creature's footprint; in his left a painting of the Bigfoot's head,* **ABOVE:** *A footprint in snow, assumed to have been made by a Bigfoot, found at Bossburg, Washington State, in 1969. The footprint was over 16½in (42cm) long, and was one of over a thousand others found at the same time. Not too much credence can be attached to Bigfoot footprints found in snow; normal human footprints in snow can be vastly enlarged as the sun's heat melts the snow. However, it is rare for humans to run around in the snow in their bare feet!*

Several frames from the famous movie shot in 1967 at Bluff Creek, California, by Roger Patterson, apparently showing a female Bigfoot, Orthodox naturalists have analyzed this film and concluded that Patterson was being hoaxed. Others take the film to be genuine, and are militant in its support; the current writer has received lengthy and abusive transatlantic telephone calls protesting about his public expression of doubts over its veracity.

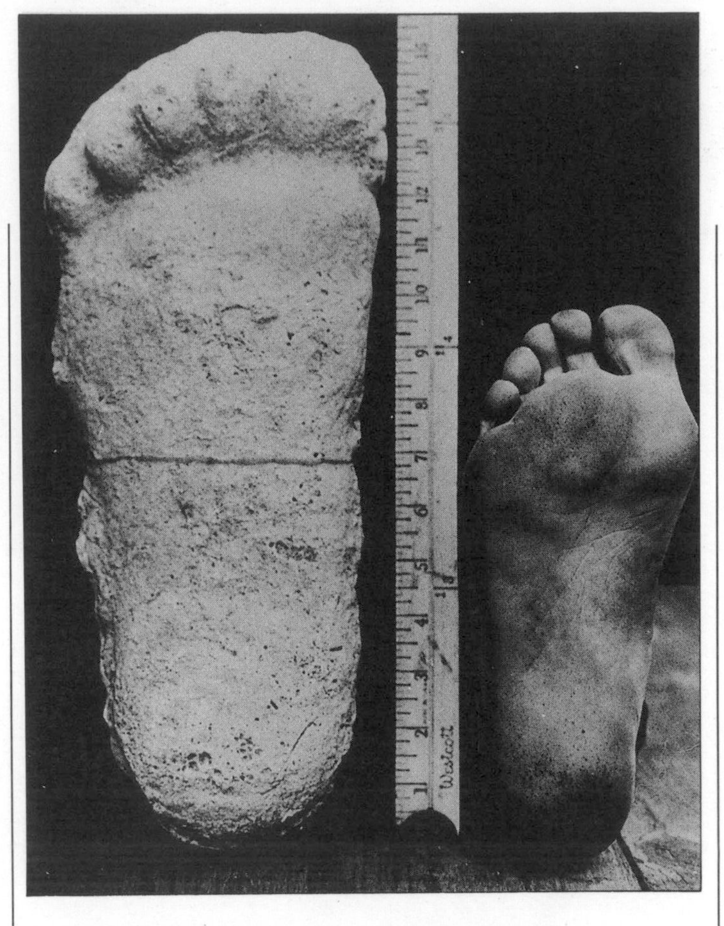

that Bigfoot might indeed be a survival of Neanderthal-type prehumans – exterminated, perhaps, by the more aggressive Cro-Magnon types in but all the most hostile regions. However, this is mere speculation: apart from anything else, we have no reason to believe that Neanderthal Man was hairy.

It is worth remembering at this point that there are other humanlike creatures that are frightened of human beings. For a considerable while reports of encounters with them in Africa were treated with derision in the West. The reference is, of course, to the gorilla, orangutan and the other large apes. It is perfectly reasonable to think that some of the apes may have a far wider range of habitats than we currently suppose. Moreover, there may be apes of which science as yet knows nothing. This may seem incredible, but remember that it was only a few decades ago that zoologists were smugly saying that every large mammal in the world was known to them – and then the okapi, which is about the size of a horse, was discovered.

If we accept that reclusive humanlike creatures exist, what do we know about their natures? First, the matter of their popularly-assumed ferocity. In this context, it is worth noting Don Whillans' testimony. He told the Sherpas on his expedition that he had seen a Yeti, and later he led them past the trail of footprints in the snow that he discovered. To his fascination, the Sherpas totally ignored them. His impression was that the Sherpas regarded the Yeti as a creature which, if you left it alone, would leave you alone. Far from being terrified of it, as so many sensationalist accounts would have us believe, the Sherpas instead display caution and respect towards it – much as we might regard a gorilla. The overall impression is that a Yeti might be dangerous if cornered, but otherwise need cause no fears.

This puts the Yeti into a rather different category from most other folk monsters, which are credited with rather nasty habits, such as eating people. The same is even more true of the Almas, viewed by the peoples of Central Asia as a lesser form of human being, but in no way a malevolent one – indeed, if we are to believe the various accounts, people in those parts treat any Almas they come across rather as one might treat a friendly dog one met in the street. These attitudes towards the assumed wild people tend to make one believe that the peoples of the various parts of Asia from which encounters have been reported are indeed telling the truth, rather than, as has so often been suggested, telling a good tale for the benefit of Western visitors.

The Sasquatch is, as it were, the North American branch of the family. It is, of course, only fair to say at once that sceptics have considerable doubts about the very existence of the Sasquatch – doubts shared by some, but far from all, of the general public.

For example, in Skamania County, Washington State, it has been thought necessary to set a fine of $10,000 as punishment for the crime of killing a Sasquatch. As yet, no cases have come to court, and it is reasonable to assume that that none ever will and that the whole affair was intended more to attract tourism than as a piece of meaningful legislation.

To date the most famous appearance of a Sasquatch has been in an amateur film taken by Roger Patterson. In the

ABOVE: *A human male foot compared with a cast made after Roger Patterson's sighting of a supposed Bigfoot in 1967.* **RIGHT:** *Bob Gimlin, Roger Patterson's companion, displaying plastercasts made by the alleged Bigfoot which Patterson had filmed. the footprints were 14½in (37cm) long.* **FAR RIGHT:** *Bigfoot investigator René Dahinden beside a sculpture of Bigfoot created by Jim McClarin at Willow Creek, California.*

autumn of 1967 he was out riding with a friend in northern California when a female Sasquatch suddenly emerged from the trees ahead of them. Patterson's horse immediately threw him, but luckily he was still clutching his cine camera and had sufficient presence of mind to shoot some film – around 20-23 ft (6-7 m) – as the creature rather lazily ran off. This film has been shown countless times over the years, and has on occasion been analysed by professional naturalists.

The verdict returned by the naturalists is rather depressing. Although the creature is quite apparently a female (it has clearly visible breasts) its gait is like that of a man. It has pronounced human-like buttocks, unlike the apes. Foot-size and stride-length do not match up (although obviously such a judgement involves preconceptions as to the relationship between the foot-size and stride-length). Damningly, its stride, as can be seen from the film, is more like that of someone attempting to make their strides as long as possible than that of a creature moving naturally.

The inevitable conclusion would seem to be that Patterson's film was a hoax. However, there is a problem here: Patterson was most manifestly convinced that what he filmed was exactly what he saw. The various researchers who have interviewed him are unanimous that he is utterly genuine about this. The only possible explanation – unless the naturalists, not all of whom are unsympathetic to the notion that the Sasquatch may exist, are wrong about the evidence of the film – is that Patterson himself was the victim of a hoax. This seems quite possible, since the top half of the filmed creature is, overall, bigger and bulkier than the bottom half would suggest it ought to be: such a creature would be a quadruped rather than a biped. One could guess – although one might be quite wrong – that Patterson's companion, Bob Gimlin, set up the incident. In the words of one naturalist who has commented on the affair, Bob Gimlin was 'somewhat of a "third man" character in this affair'. However, it should be stressed that it is far from proven that there was any hoaxing involved: unknown animals, almost by definition, will break some of the general rules inferred by naturalists from their observations of known animals.

Even if Patterson's film was the product of a hoax, a single piece of trickery does not mean that *all* stories of the Sasquatch are fallacious. A very convincing piece of evidence comes from an encounter in 1917 between an

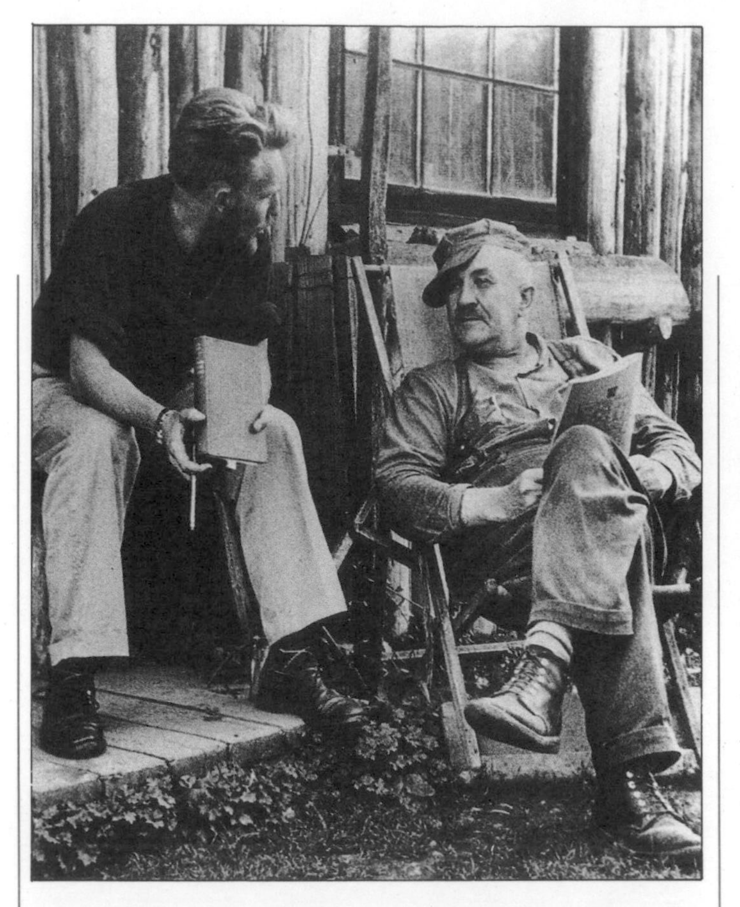

expedition led by a Swiss geologist, François de Loys, and a couple of large primates on the Venezuela/Colombia border. The primates were aggressive towards the humans, screaming shrilly and eventually defaecating into their own hands so that they could hurl excrement – a typical aggressive response of the larger primates. Finally the humans, who were terrified, shot at the male, although in fact it was the female that they killed (the male ran off).

The humans photographed the corpse, and from the photograph we can deduce that the primate was of the order of 5 ft (1.5 m) tall. De Loys himself measured the height as 5 ft 1¾ in (1.57 m), which certainly put the creature firmly into the height-range of adult human beings – and, likewise, meant that it was far larger than any known New World primate. Moreover, the size of the forehead and the dentition indicated that this creature was only remotely, if at all, related to the known primates of the Americas; and its overall appearance is definitely humanoid. At least one naturalist has suggested that the creature represents an advanced ape, evolving independently in the Americas, of roughly the same status as *Pithecanthropus erectus*.

Or, perhaps, the primate concerned was actually a member of a surviving colony of primitive human beings (such as *Pithecanthropus*), living advisedly far from *Homo sapiens* in the least-travelled parts of Latin America? This is far from beyond the bounds of possibility. However, there is one interesting point. The creature in de Loys' photograph, while definitely female, has the flat breasts typical of apes. By contrast, the female Yeti are widely reported by the Sherpas to have breasts so huge and droopy that they have to throw them back over their shoulders in order to run. It is likely that the Sherpa tales are, in this respect, exaggerated; but nevertheless the very fact that the exaggeration should be promulgated suggests that Yeti females have, like their human counterparts, protuberant breasts. They are, therefore, a long way – speaking in terms of evolution – from the gorillas, chimps, orangutans and other higher primates. They are much more like us.

The photograph taken by de Loys' expedition provides virtual proof that unknown anthropoids dwell in the Americas, and so it does not seem too ridiculous to believe that at least some of the reported Sasquatch sightings are perfectly genuine. One of these days a live Bigfoot may be, however unwillingly, brought to meet its more 'advanced' fellows, although in a way one hopes that this never comes about. Bigfoot may not have developed a technology capable of curing killer diseases and manufacturing digital watches; on the other hand, it has yet to invent nuclear warfare.

Let us hope that, should the existence of Bigfoot finally be proved, we treat our 'fellows' humanely, rather than hunt them down and exterminate them as, for example, the Europeans destroyed the indigenous Tasmanians during the 19th century. Perhaps Bigfoot is wise to hide in the remote parts of the world.

There are, then, several possible explanations of the Bigfoot mystery. Since the reports from different parts of the world vary quite dramatically in their details, it is quite possible that all of the explanations may be correct, and that attempts to produce a unified theory are born from the human impulse to rationalize things. There could be a reclusive culture of hirsute humans in the high Himalayas *and* unknown species of primates in South America; we may simply be compounding several mysteries into one.

ABOVE: *Albert Ostman, on the right, being interviewed by John Green. Ostman claimed that in 1924 he had been abducted by a family of Sasquatches in British Columbia. Despite the apparent implausibility of the tale, and the fact that he waited until 1957 to tell it, circumstantial details of his account have convinced many people who are normally sceptics that he was indeed telling the truth.* **RIGHT:** *The corpse of a strangely manlike animal killed by François de Loys and his party on the Venezuela/Colombia border in 1917. This creature is unknown to science. It is impossible to determine whether it is an ape or a hominid.*

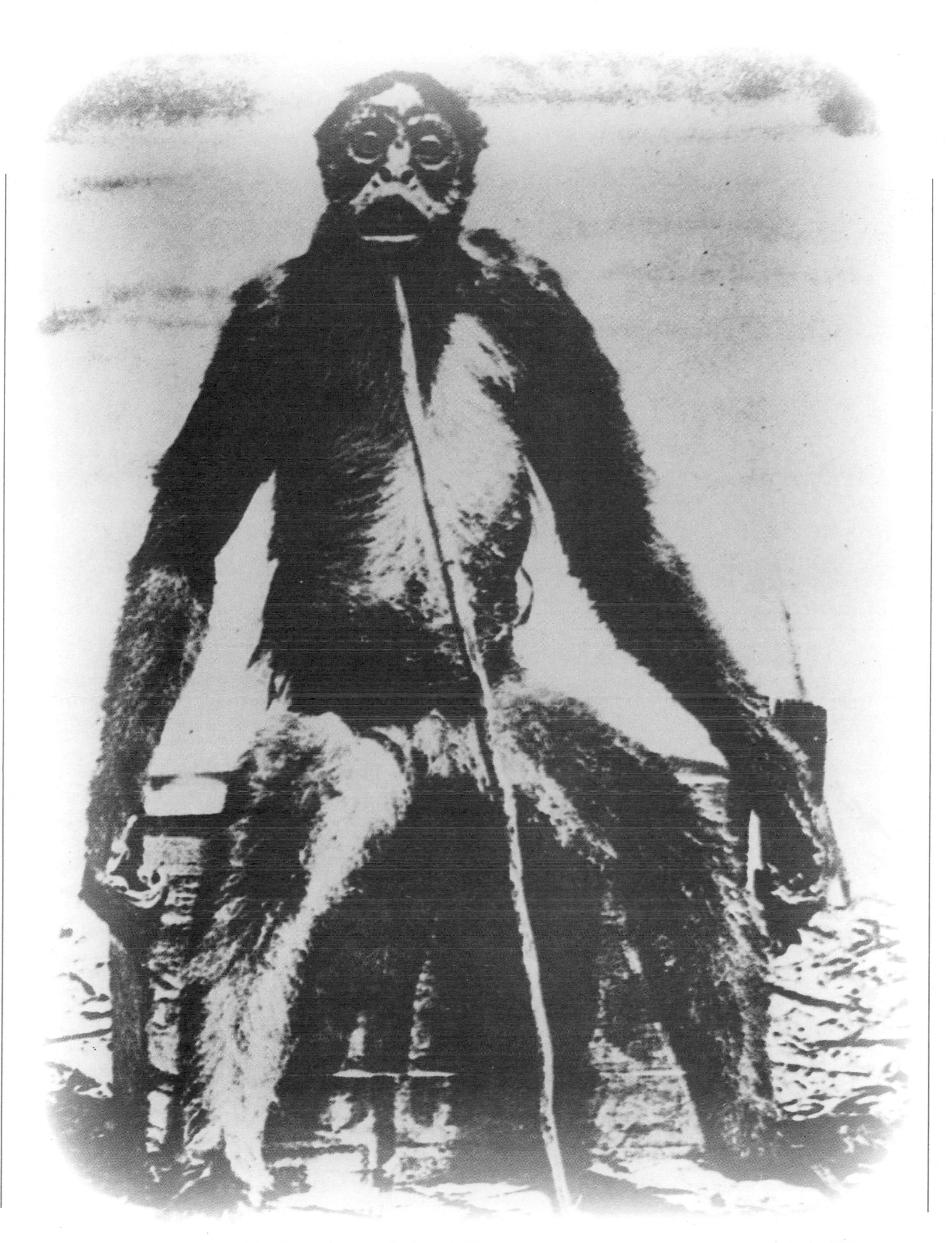

LITTLE PEOPLE

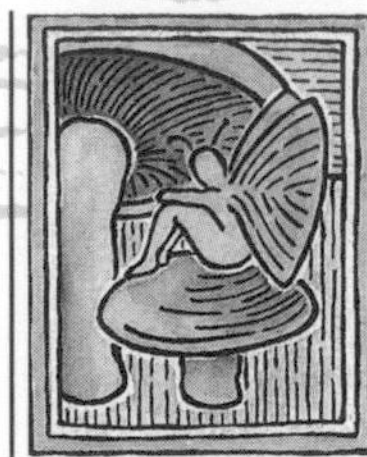

BETWEEN 1917 AND 1920 two young girls, Frances Griffiths and her cousin, Elsie Wright, took a series of astonishing photographs in a 'fairy glen' at the back of Elsie's house in Cottingley, Yorkshire. These photographs purported to show the girls playing with elves and fairies – who came complete with wings and merry expressions, just like the fairies in Victorian children's books. Sir Arthur Conan Doyle, whose interest in matters psychic was intense, publicized the case, and since then the 'Cottingley Fairies' have become established in the literature.

It is still said that no scientific test has been able to prove that these photographs were faked. This is curious, because merely by looking at them you can see sufficient discrepancies of focus and perspective to indicate that the 'fairies' are paper cut-outs. This the two hoaxers admitted themselves in later life.

A further reason for doubting the photographs had always been that the idea of fairies as ethereal miniatures is a comparatively recent one. The little people – elementals – were traditionally regarded as something rather different: they were troglodytic spirits, about the size of a 10-year-old human child, and far from being friendly and playful they could be very unpleasant indeed, if crossed. They possessed formidable spiritual powers, and some varieties had

exceedingly nasty habits; for example, redcaps got their name because of their practice of dying their caps in travellers' blood. Leprechauns and brownies, who are positively helpful to human beings, are very much in the minority.

A number of writers have linked fairies to the UFO phenomenon. Some have taken a 'physical' approach, suggesting that all the traditional tales of fairies are really accounts of the activities of visiting Little Green Men. Others have suggested, as we have seen in connection with lake monsters (*see* page 82), that each age and culture produces its own supernatural object which observers are capable of reifying, or, at the very least, of *believing* that they see. (The distinction between the two latter hypotheses may be an artificial one, if we are to take at face value some of the ideas of modern physics.)

Another theory is that there genuinely did coexist with humanity a race of smaller, humanoid, intelligent creatures, and it is very tempting to suggest that this might be a product of the experiences of our Cro-Magnon-type ancestors with the surviving remnants of Neanderthal-type humans. Of course, folk-memories do last a long time, and so the theory cannot be thrown out completely. However, like so many superficially attractive ideas, it suffers from a complete lack of supporting evidence.

Do fairies exist? Alternatively, did they exist in historical times, but have now died out? This is a genuine mystery, and one that may never be solved. However, it seems likely that the 'physical' explanation is erroneous, in that no one has yet unearthed a fossil fairy. Or is the belief in little people a necessary part of the human psyche? It seems that most of us have to believe that the universe is, as it were, made up of 'us' and 'them', and fairies are good candidates for 'them'.

LEFT: AND RIGHT: *Two typical examples of the faked series of 'Cottingley Fairy' photographs. Surprisingly, these pictures for decades hoodwinked otherwise sober individuals.* **UPPER LEFT:** *A fairy ring, as depicted in Olaus Magnus' Historia de Gentibus Septentrionalibus, 1558. The depiction of the 'little people' could hardly be more different from that in the 'Cottingley Fairy' forgeries, which were a product of the romanticized image of fairies generated during the Victorian era. Here the emphasis is both animalistic and sexual; note the juxtaposition of a serpent with the fairy at* **TOP LEFT. BACKGROUND:** *Fairies dancing, from an old English Chapbook.*

MIRACLES

IN MAY 1917 THREE young children were looking after sheep near Fátima, Portugal. The three had not long gone through the rosary when, after a few flashes of lightning, the Virgin Mary appeared before them. She asked the children to return to the site on the 13th of each month until October of that year, at which time she would tell them why she had come. On the next appointed day, 13 June, about 60 people were with the children, and they saw very little, although the eldest child, Lucia Santos, held a deeply religious conversation with an invisible entity. On being asked if the three children would soon be escorted to Heaven, the entity said that Lucia's two companions, her cousins Francisco and Jacinta Marto, would indeed shuffle off this mortal coil in the near future, but that Lucia herself would remain on earth for some while longer. (This proved to be true: thanks to the great influenza epidemic of 1919, Francisco died in that year and Jacinta in the following one, yet Lucia lived to a ripe old age.)

The meeting on 13 July was attended by a crowd of about 5,000, and that in August by about 20,000. The latter fell completely flat because the sub-prefect of the region had decided to imprison the children for the relevant day. However, on their release, the children had a vision of the Virgin on the 19th day of the month; this time the Virgin said that the promised October revelation would be rather less than expected, because of the failure to keep up the meetings on each 13th day of the month, but that it would still be fairly sensational; she also requested that the children pressurize for a chapel to be built.

RIGHT: *The three children at the heart of the Fátima miracles. From left to right, they are Jacinta, Francisco and Lucia.* **BELOW:** *A selection of the crowd viewing the reported solar phenomena witnessed at Fátima on 13 October 1917.*

JACINTA
FRANCISCO
LUCIA

Along came 13 September, and this time there were as many as 30,000 spectators present. Some were disappointed, seeing nothing except Lucia talking to empty air, but others noted rose-petals falling to the ground and the presence of a curious ball of light 'gliding', according to one witness, 'slowly and majestically through space'.

The apparition of 13 October was obviously going to be the big one, and no fewer than 70,000 people turned out to watch it. There was such a crush that the three children had some difficulty in fighting their way through to the meeting-place. Lucia conversed with the Virgin, and then saw the entire Holy Family in the sky, just next to the sun. She exhorted the crowd to look in that direction: according to about half of the observers, the sun then cavorted in a pinwheel fashion around the sky. The other half of the crowd saw nothing of interest.

Lucia lived on to become a nun, and in her memoirs, fully published in 1942, she claimed several further supernatural encounters. There seems to be little doubt that she

genuinely believed in her visitations by members of the Holy Family; yet, equally, it seems unlikely that it happened. Moreover, although there were countless press photographers present at the final Fátima vision, not one of them seems to have been moved to photograph the sun jumping around the sky. (A much-reproduced picture is actually of an earlier solar eclipse, and was taken in a quite different part of the world.)

Whatever went on in the mind of Lucia Santos in 1917, we can describe the whole series of events as being, together, a miracle. But what exactly do we mean by the word 'miracle'? One dictionary provides as a definition 'a marvellous event attributed to a supernatural cause'. This hardly helps us explain miracles; slightly to pervert a statement of Arthur C Clarke, any effect produced by a technology beyond our comprehension is, by definition, miraculous, so that merely to ascribe miracles to the 'supernatural' is to dodge the issue, rather as if we said 'it's all done by physics'.

Yet miracles do seem to occur. Sai Baba of Puttaparti is probably the most 'miraculous' person of the 20th century. Whereas other yogis perform miracles only occasionally and often in dubious circumstances, Baba executes wonders on the large scale, often in front of teams of respectable witnesses or vast crowds of ordinary believers. Moreover that rarest of things in the supernatural world – he performs his miracles on demand.

According to various reports, Baba can materialize objects from nowhere, levitate, perform acts of psychokinesis, and display many other startling abilities. At his ashram, close by Puttaparti, thousands throng every year to see him at work. Most of his miracles are connected with healing. His most astonishing reported feat to date is the raising of a young man from the dead. In fact, it is claimed that he has done this several times, but only once has the miracle been performed under stringent scientific checks. Interestingly, Baba claims to be an avatar, meaning that he has roughly the same relation to the deity as did Jesus Christ; one of Christ's most famous miracles was the raising of a young man, Lazarus, from the dead.

Images of the Virgin Mary are widely reported to move, weep and generally perform miracles. **TOP LEFT:** *A statue of the Virgin, blood pouring from her eyes, photographed in 1972 in Porto San Stefano, Italy,* **LEFT:** *A 1984 photograph, taken in Brooklyn, New York, of a statue of Mary apparently weeping. It goes without saying that conventional science has no explanation for such phenomena – assuming that is, that they are not hoaxes.* **ABOVE RIGHT:** *Sai Baba of Puttaparti – a man for whom, if all accounts are to be believed, miracles are everyday occurrences. Witnesses of his deeds have included many highly reputable people, who are unlikely to have clubbed together to spread a hoax. It is difficult to equate some of Baba's feats – such as raising a person from the dead – with our everyday notions of 'common sense'.*

Baba is a healer and psychic surgeon, too. The Tasmanian journalist, Howard Murphet, in his biography, *Sai Baba: Man of Miracles*, tells of a number of instances in which he personally watched Baba at work. In one well attested case Baba was able to cure a patient suffering from terminal cancer – although this is perhaps less miraculous than some of his other feats, in that cancer is almost certainly at least partly psychosomatic.

Baba is, apparently, a cheerful fellow, and welcomes visitors – even sceptical ones – with smiles and jokes. Unlike many other assumed miracle-workers, he does not refuse to prove his abilities in front of cynics: often he will produce for them a handful of sacred ash which he has materialized before their very eyes. To others he gives photographs of himself from which, from time to time over succeeding years, sacred ash will spontaneously materialize.

Of course, it is impossible to produce even tentative explanations of miracles: by definition, they are inexplicable. Moreover, the two types of miracle discussed here are vastly different – Lucia's religious visions are, quite literally, a world away from Baba's materializations and levitations. All we can say is that the latter type of miracle seems to have a lot in common with psychokinesis (*see* page 36). The former is certainly outside the province of any form of scientific investigation.

Unidentified Flying Objects

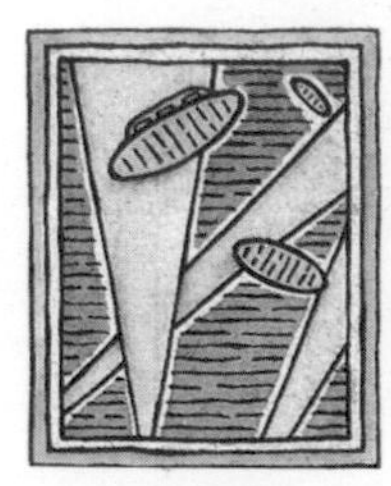

The roman historian, Livy (59BC-AD17) seems to have been a great enthusiast for celestial happenings, for he recorded about 30 unusual things observed in the skies. It seems unlikely that he himself saw any of these – most had occurred long before his time – yet the accounts he gives could, with only minor changes, be mistaken for modern UFO reports. For example, he describes how skyships were witnessed in 218BC and how, four years later, a vision of men in white clothes gathered round an altar was seen in the skies over Hadria.

Generally speaking, the history of UFOs is traced back to 24 June 1947, when a pilot called Kenneth Arnold was flying his private plane near Mount Rainier, in Washington State, and saw nine gleaming discs swooping in and out of the peaks of the Cascade Mountains. He later described the motion of the discs as being much like that of a saucer 'skipped' across water; and the term 'flying saucer' was born. But reports of UFOs go back long before that, as we have seen. There is even claimed to be one in the Old Testament, in *Ezekiel:*

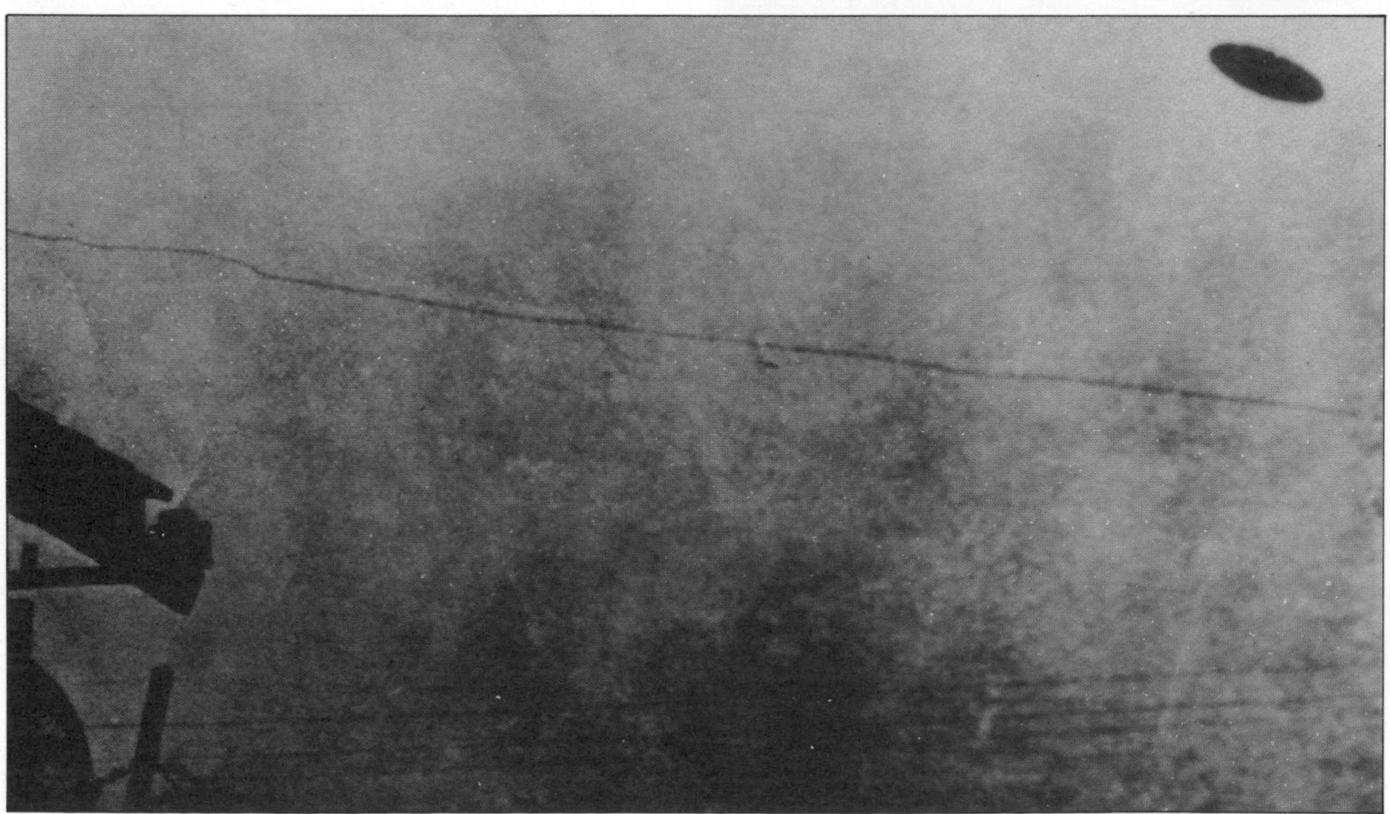

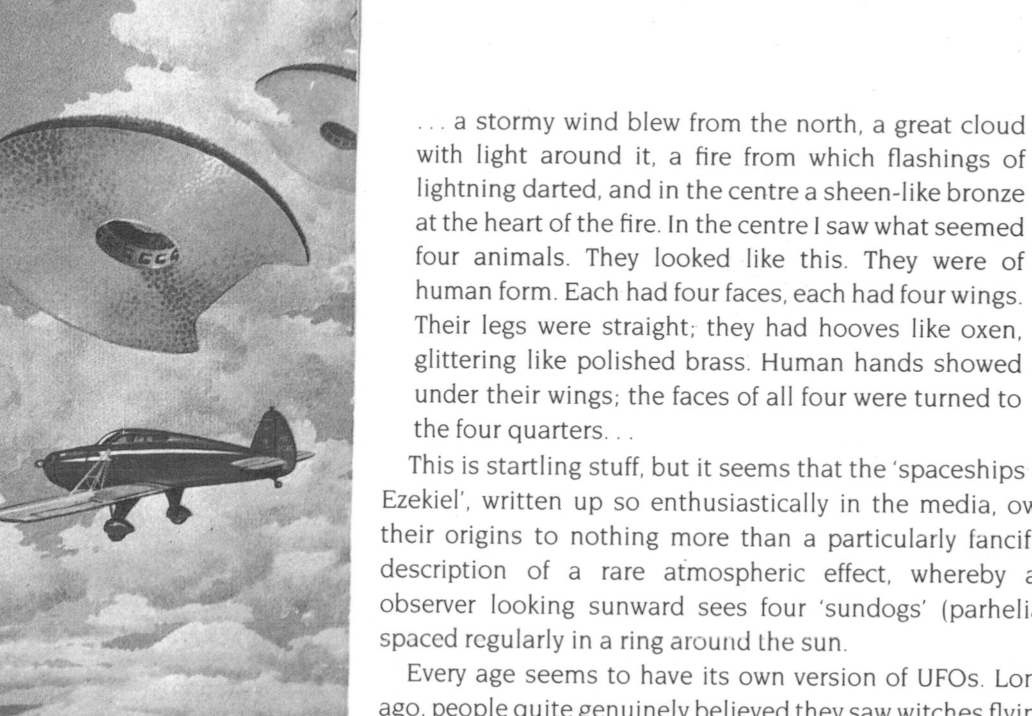

> . . . a stormy wind blew from the north, a great cloud with light around it, a fire from which flashings of lightning darted, and in the centre a sheen-like bronze at the heart of the fire. In the centre I saw what seemed four animals. They looked like this. They were of human form. Each had four faces, each had four wings. Their legs were straight; they had hooves like oxen, glittering like polished brass. Human hands showed under their wings; the faces of all four were turned to the four quarters. . .

This is startling stuff, but it seems that the 'spaceships of Ezekiel', written up so enthusiastically in the media, owe their origins to nothing more than a particularly fanciful description of a rare atmospheric effect, whereby an observer looking sunward sees four 'sundogs' (parhelia) spaced regularly in a ring around the sun.

Every age seems to have its own version of UFOs. Long ago, people quite genuinely believed they saw witches flying through the skies on broomsticks. During the winter and spring of 1896-97 there were widespread reports of an airship flying over North America; it took about five months

LEFT: *A photograph taken in May 1951 by the Trent family of McMinnville, Oregon, showing the UFO which they observed. This is one of the very few UFO photographs to have passed all scientific tests – including recent examinations using computer enhancement.* **ABOVE LEFT:** *Kenneth Arnold.* **ABOVE:** *The Spring 1948 issue of Fate – the very first edition of the magazine – showed an illustration of Arnold's encounter that relied considerably on artistic licence.* **RIGHT:** *One of the rarer of the dozens of photographs produced by George Adamski, showing a cigar-shaped 'mothership' and several 'scout craft'. Most modern ufologists believe that this, like others produced by Adamski, was a fake.*

to cross the country from west to east. In terms of cultural history, this case is particularly interesting, because in 1896 the airship had roughly the same status in the popular consciousness as the spaceship has today: you know they exist, but you would be mighty surprised to see one.

It is true that a great deal of nonsense is talked on the subject of UFOs. For example, in 1975 Marshall Herff Applewhite and Bonnie Lu Trusdale Nettles, generally known as 'Bo' and 'Peep', told the world that they had come to this planet by UFO from 'the level above human'; their objective was to enlist as many humans as possible in 'the Process' and then to return, with these acolytes, to the 'higher level'. A notable point was that, if you wanted to join 'the Process', all you had to do was to hand over all your worldly goods to Bo and Peep. These two worthies claimed that within about six months their physical bodies would be assassinated, but that their spirits would live on to guide their disciples skywards. As many as 1,000 people at any one time believed this stuff, although after Bo and Peep failed to be assassinated on schedule the numbers dropped off.

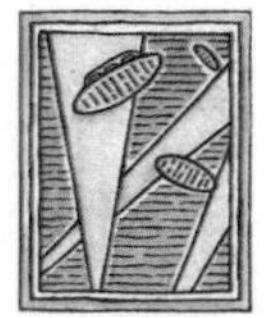

Various UFO photographs, all probably fakes, **LEFT AND RIGHT:** *In 1963 and 1966 Paul Villa claimed that he chatted with alien astronauts who arrived in these two discs. Perhaps they should have let their tentacles do the walking.* **ABOVE:** *A spinning UFO photographed in Oregon in 1964: all resemblances to a light fitting are totally coincidental.* **TOP FAR RIGHT:** *A claimed UFO photographed in 1954 in Coniston, Cumbria, England.* **TOP RIGHT:** *A claimed UFO photographed in 1952 in Passiac, New Jersey.*

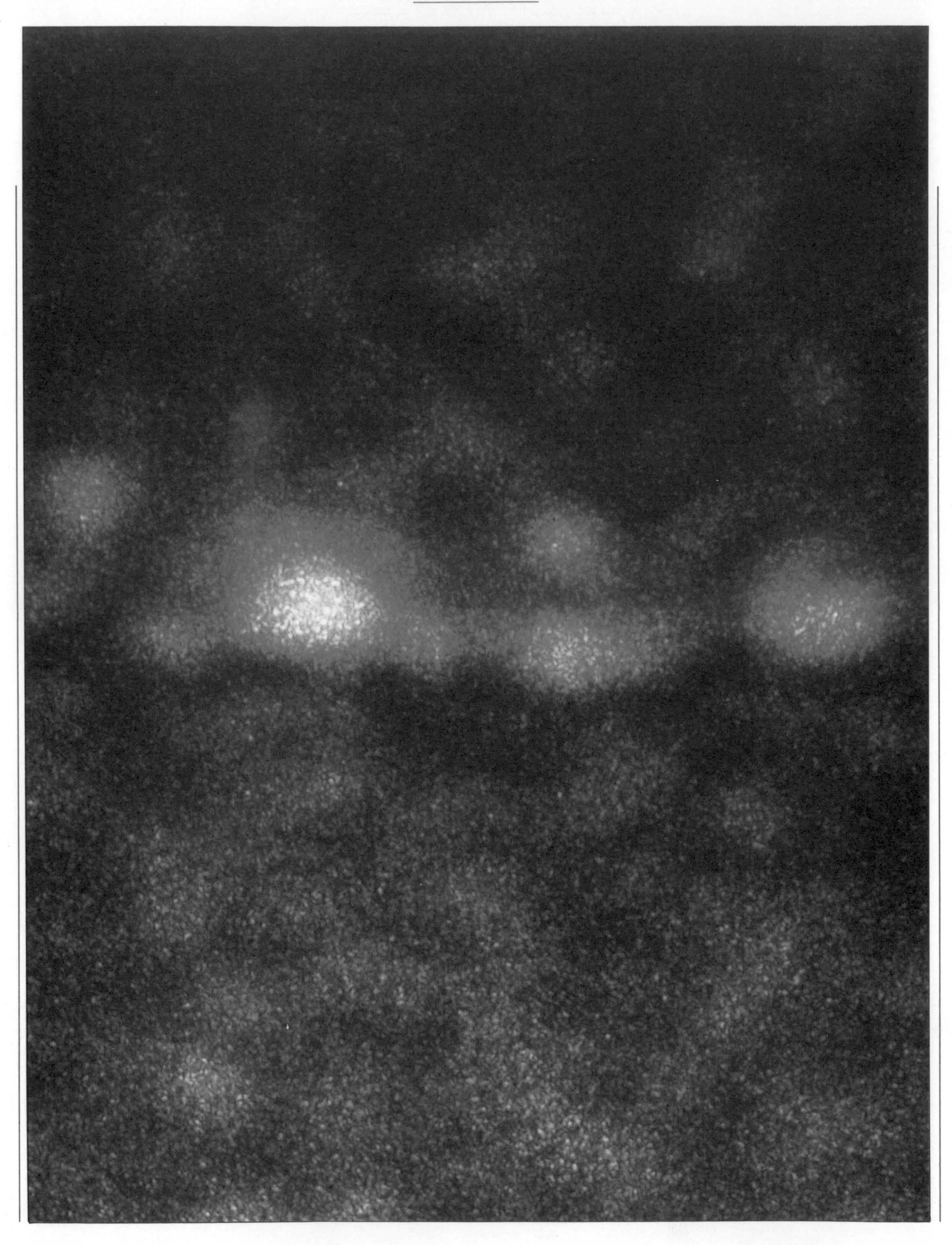

UFO hoaxes abound. A deliberate spoof, *An Account of a Meeting with Denizens of Another World, 1871* (1979) by 'William Loosley', has been quoted as genuine by the credulous, as has *Flying Saucer from Mars* (1955) by 'Cedric Allingham'. T. Lobsang Rampa, the famous Tibetan sage and author of books such as *The Third Eye* (1956), otherwise known as the Irish hoaxer, Cyril Hoskin, tells us the Revealed Truth. UFOs are actually spaceships visiting from a world made out of antimatter. This is why they never touch down: matter and antimatter explode with colossal ferocity on contact. The trouble with Rampa's explanation is that air, too, is made out of matter.

Moreover, there are quite a few reports of UFOs touching down. The most famous concern the claims of Californian soft-drinks salesman, George Adamski, who had a number of 'close encounters'. Much of the associated evidence suggests that Adamski was either very imaginative or, shall we say, an entrepreneur. However, there are two follow-ups to Adamski's story that are little known, and both are interesting

First, 24 hours after Adamski's death in 1964, a man called Edward Bryant was walking in open country in Devon, England, when he came across a 'parked' UFO. One of the aliens from the craft, an individual with a boyish appearance, introduced himself to Bryant as 'Yamski' and asked Bryant to give his regards to 'Des' or 'Les'. Now, it was unlikely that Bryant could have heard of Adamski's death by the time of his alleged encounter. Moreover, according to Adamski's first co-author, the journalist, Desmond Leslie ('Des' or 'Les'?), only he and a few others knew that the ufonauts had promised Adamski that he would on death pay a speedy return visit to earth in the form of a young boy.

Unfortunately, Bryant failed to tell his story until some weeks later, by which time the whole affair had become a lot less miraculous. At least one ufologist who worked on the case was convinced that Bryant was lying, and his partner in the investigation, although more sympathetic, was careful to point out that the possibility of Bryant inventing the story was a very real one. Sadly, Bryant died only a couple of years after his alleged encounter, and so we cannot ask him.

The second curious follow-up to the Adamski case occurred in 1980, with the discovery in northern England – Todmorden, West Yorkshire, to be precise – of the body of a man. This man had disappeared some days earlier. His trousers were ripped, and his shirt was missing. He had some superficial cuts on his hands and knees and a scrape on his right thigh. Perhaps more significantly, he had a curious burn-mark on his head – it seemed to be an acid burn – which, according to the post mortem, had occurred some two days before his death and appeared to have been treated with some form of ointment. The man had not been living as a tramp during the time between his disappearance and the discovery of his corpse: for example, he had only a one-day stubble, despite having been missing for five days.

The whole case is a mystery, and still no one knows for certain what happened. It also sparked off a UFO 'flap', for various understandable reasons. Jenny Randles, who has written the standard book on the affair, gives a chronology: on 6 June the man disappeared; on 7 June a huge ball of orange light was seen in the nearby city of Bradford; similar lights were seen in Todmorden itself and neighbouring Halifax on 8 June; on 9 and 10 June there were many reports

LEFT: *Modern, scientific ufologists have little brief for tales of abductions by extraterrestrials, instead regarding the various phenomena as having diverse sources. This photograph shows an example of a UAP (unidentified atmospheric phenomenon) witnessed in a remote Norwegian valley at Hessdalen, near the Arctic Circle. These blobs of light appear repeatedly in the valley, yet various scientific expeditions have failed to determine their origin or nature. That the lights exist is proved by the countless photographs of them which have been taken. As to what they are, no one yet has a clue.* **ABOVE:** *Jenny Randles, one of the most widely respected ufologists of modern times. Her objectivity has earned the regard of even convinced sceptics*

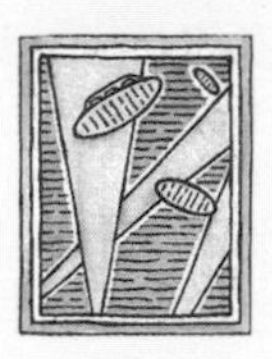

Some of the more impressive UFO photographs are those where it was only later that the photographer noted the presence of a UFO. **LEFT:** *Japanese news photographer Tsutomu Nakayama took this shot in Hawaii in April 1974, and only when it was developed did he notice the UFO.* **TOP RIGHT:** *Wilfred Power, had a very similar experience when he thought he was photographing nothing more than a giraffe at Plymouth Zoo, Devon, England.* **ABOVE AND RIGHT:** *Two frequently reproduced photograhs purporting to show flying saucers. One is probably of reflections of lights in the windows of the laboratory from which it was taken; the other is a lenticular cloud formation.*

of celestial lights from the region south of Bradford; and on 11 June the corpse was discovered. The curious circumstances of the case, coupled with all this UFO activity, made it inevitable that UFOs would be related to the bizarre death. But there was a third factor: the deceased's name was Zigmund Adamski.

There is no suggestion that Zigmund was any relation of George, yet Adamski is not a common name in Great Britain. A curious coincidence, or something more? It is hard to tell. Yet it is worth noting that irritating little parallels like this one occur throughout the field of the paranormal.

Two UFO cases stand alone as the most widely reported of all. One is the Tunguska explosion of 1908 and the other is the 'interrupted journey' of Betty and Barney Hill in 1961.

The Tunguska forest is in a remote part of Siberia. Early on 30 June 1908 the few people of the region saw a fireball zooming through the air, leaving a trail of smoke and changing course at least once before exploding with a violence equivalent to about 20 megatons. Fortunately, because the region was – and is – so sparsely populated, few if any people lost their lives, although the slaughter among the animal population was horrific. From the point of view of science, though, the remoteness of the area and the sparseness of population combined to ensure that 20 years were to pass before a scientific expedition from Moscow arrived. The scientists expected to find a meteoritic impact crater. Instead they found good evidence that the object had indeed, just as the peasants reported, exploded in the air. Vast areas of trees had been blown flat, all lying pointing outwards from the blast's obvious epicentre. The scientists discovered many other curiosities – although not quite so many as are listed in the more popular accounts of the affair.

BELOW: *Betty and Barney Hill, the two most famous UFO contactees of all time.*
RIGHT: *Each year between 1954 and 1977 alleged UFO contactee George Van Tassell organized the Giant Rock Convention in California; his claim was that the Giant Rock area naturally attracted UFOs. This photograph was taken in 1970 in the area by Reserve Sheriff W A Ackerman. The pedestrians seem surprisingly unconcerned by the apparition.*

The opinion of orthodox science is that the object which fell in 1908 was a very small comet. This would explain, for example, the curious discoveries of deposits of anomalous chemical elements at the blast's 'ground zero'. Also, it is perfectly possible that a comet, entering the atmosphere from the cold, unpressurized wastes of space, would explode before reaching the ground. It is *just* possible that, through differential ablation, the comet might change course as it soared through the skies.

However, in the late 1940s the idea emerged that the object might have been an extraterrestrial spacecraft, whose occupants, realizing that the machine was getting wildly out of control and that the engine was about to explode, succeeded in steering it to a remote part of the globe – either to spare human life or simply out of a desire for secrecy.

The case of Betty and Barney Hill is of special interest because it has been so widely documented: the standard book on the subject is John Fuller's *The Interrupted Journey*

(1966). In 1961 the Hills were driving home when they saw a light in the sky which they thought might be a UFO. They did not think too much about it until they reached home, when they discovered that somehow they had 'lost' a few hours. Even so, it is easy enough to be mistaken about the time. But then Betty began to have some extraordinary dreams: she was on board a spacecraft, being examined by extra-terrestrials. Under hypnosis, she recounted the details of the event, saying that this was no dream, but had actually happened during those 'lost' two hours. Many years later she was to produce a star-map, drawn from her memory of one shown to her by the aliens, which she said indicated the star of their origin, Eta Reticuli. This map, in fact, is of no value: *any* pattern of dots can be matched up to the night sky somewhere, and experiments done with a random-number generator have produced much better representations of the region of Eta Reticuli than Betty's. Yet why should Betty be prompted to draw a star-map?

It is interesting that Barney's experience was somewhat different. Obviously his wife told him about her vivid dreams, and in due course he came to believe that the events depicted therein had actually happened. However, even under hypnosis, he was able to give only the vaguest of details about these assumed events. The psychiatrist who worked with the Hills was convinced that the whole affair was a product solely of Betty's mind.

The most fashionistic view of UFOs today is that they are all the product of people's minds. This is not to say that observers are simply 'seeing things', although obviously a lot of UFO sightings owe their origins to genuine misinterpretations of natural phenomena (ball lightning, distorted views of the planet Venus, and so on). What really happens, say many modern ufologists, is that UFOs are reified – brought into reality – by the right-brains of individual human beings; once reified, the objects can be seen by other people.

LEFT: *Two versions of a photograph taken in October 1981 by Hannah McRoberts to the north of Kelsey Bay, Vancouver Island, British Columbia. Ms McRoberts was simply taking pictures of the mountain, and at the time neither she nor her companions noticed the UFO revealed in the enlargement.*

ABOVE: *A photograph taken in 1966 in New Mexico showing what purports to be a small, remote-controlled flying saucer, about 3ft (1m) in diameter. Photograhs such as this one understandably arouse deep scepticism among modern ufologists.*

This matches well with theories concerning the poltergeist effect (*see* page 44). For example, in 1948 a large glowing object was spotted over Kentucky, and three USAF pilots were sent to investigate. One of them, Thomas Mantell, got very close to the object and over the radio gave graphic descriptions of it. Then his radio transmissions ceased, and some while later the wreckage of his airplane was discovered. What was he chasing? Almost certainly, it was a weather balloon: Mantell, not equipped with oxygen, flew too high and blacked out. Yet the evidence that there were weather balloons in that area is not especially convincing. Moreover, Mantell's two colleagues, who returned safely to base, saw nothing. It is possible that Mantell was chasing a chimera born from his own mind . . . and yet he was investigating the object solely because of prior ground-based observations of it. If the object was a weather balloon, why did the other pilots not see it? If it was the product of someone's right-brain, then whose? Several decades later, we have little chance of solving this particular mystery.

That UFOs are mental, rather than straightforwardly physical, phenomena is a notion supported by the experiences during the later 1970s and early 1980s of the Sunderland family, who lived on the northern Welsh border. The mother and three of her children had many very curious UFO encounters, a few of them while awake, but most of them in dreams. Scientists were totally incapable of explaining the events, except that they were born from the minds of the Sunderlands; yet, in orthodox scientific terms, this hardly explains the waking encounters. It is easy enough to explain away the children's dramatic dreams as merely a result of an overdose of science-fiction videos, but the same does not apply to encounters *shared by more than one child*. Clearly there was some mental phenomenon at work here which we do not yet fully – or even partially – understand.

The idea that aliens might visit us is, of course, not innately foolish. It seems highly probable that there are many other civilized cultures out there in the universe, although we have no way of knowing quite how rife life, let alone intelligent life, is. During the past couple of decades a great many people have made a great deal of money out of the suggestion that aliens visited us during prehistory and promoted our intellectual development. This is possible, but to date not a single piece of convincing evidence has been produced – whatever they say on the covers of the

LEFT: *A single UFO photographed in 1982 at Hessdalen, Norway. As noted on page 105, these lights are believed to be unidentified atmospheric phenomena rather than material objects.* **ABOVE:** *A classic fake; note the poor focus.* **RIGHT:** *UFOs photographed at Conisburgh, Yorkshire, in March 1966 by Stephen Pratt, then aged 14. The precise nature of these objects must remain a matter for debate.*

paperbacks! One attractive notion is that life on earth started solely because a visiting spacecraft landed and, as it were, emptied its chemical toilets, complete with microorganisms, which over the billennia evolved to produce human beings. This is a notion much more appealing than the idea that, to take just a single example, Jesus Christ was a visitor from outer space. One's general attitude might be summarized by quoting the opening of Erich von Däniken's seminal work, *Chariots of the Gods?*: 'It took courage to write this book, and it will take courage to read it'.

Is there any possibility, then, that one day we shall encounter an extraterrestrial civilization? Sceptics point to the fact that we haven't yet; if there are, as the optimists suggest, a million technologically advanced civilizations in our own galaxy, then why have none come to visit us? Various ufologists, of course, assert that indeed they have; but this is unconvincing. The economics of travelling between the stars are frightening – just think of the cost of a single Space Shuttle mission – and so it is unlikely that extraterrestrial civilizations will expend megabucks on cheerful family tourism to a minor planet in the galaxy's backwaters.

There are various possible reasons why extraterrestrials have failed to visit us during historical times. One is that we are the only technological civilization in our corner of the

galaxy, or even in the entire universe. Another is that the distances between the stars are simply too huge for interstellar travel to be a practicable possibility. Yet again, are we not making an anthropocentric assumption in thinking that other civilizations would have the remotest interest in getting in touch with us?

But the real reason why we have heard nothing from the outside universe may be much more prosaic: we haven't been looking. The most famous attempt to pick up radio signals from other civilizations was Project Ozma in 1960: for less than 200 hours two 'probable' nearby stars were the object of attention of radioastronomers at Green Bank. The idea of this experiment was that it should merely demonstrate a principle; yet it was widely derided for its failure to record incoming alien communications. The cynics possibly did not pause to ponder the statistical likelihood that the putative civilizations associated with two stars out of billions would just happen to beam a transmission in our direction so that it would arrive some time during those eight days. The governments of the developed countries of our world (with the reputed exception of the USSR) have, however, since then unanimously decided to agree with the cynics and not 'waste money' on the search for extraterrestrial intelligence.

A final reason for our lack of contact with the assumed aliens is hardly to be taken seriously, but the theory – the product of Charles Fort's ever-fertile mind – is fun. His idea was that 'we are property' – in other words, the 'cattle' of the universe. Of course, you only bother to visit your cattle when you need to, and so far our owners have not needed to. But there may come a time.

Seeking out UFOs can be a chilly business. This 1984 photograph shows the basecamp for Project Hessdalen, whose task was to investigate the mysterious lights seen there.

LOST LANDS

THE LIST OF REPUTED lost lands – continents, countries or cities that have disappeared or have 'locked themselves away' behind some impenetrable supernatural barrier – is virtually endless. The most famous of all is Atlantis; runners-up are Mu and Lemuria. But lands such as Avalon, Shangri-La and the Gardens of the Hesperides are well known, too. One of particular interest is the city of Troy, long believed to be a myth. Its remains were finally tracked down by Arthur Schliemann in 1870, showing that some tales of lost lands are not as foolish as they may seem. What is not generally known is that this 'mighty city' was in fact the size of the average modern village.

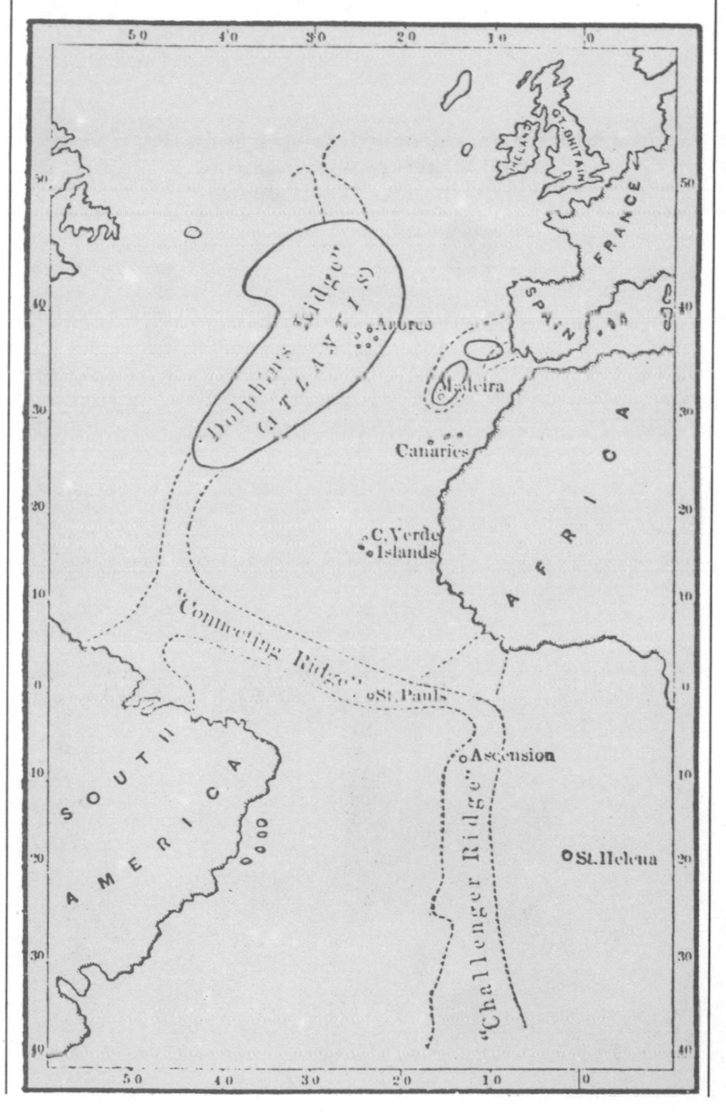

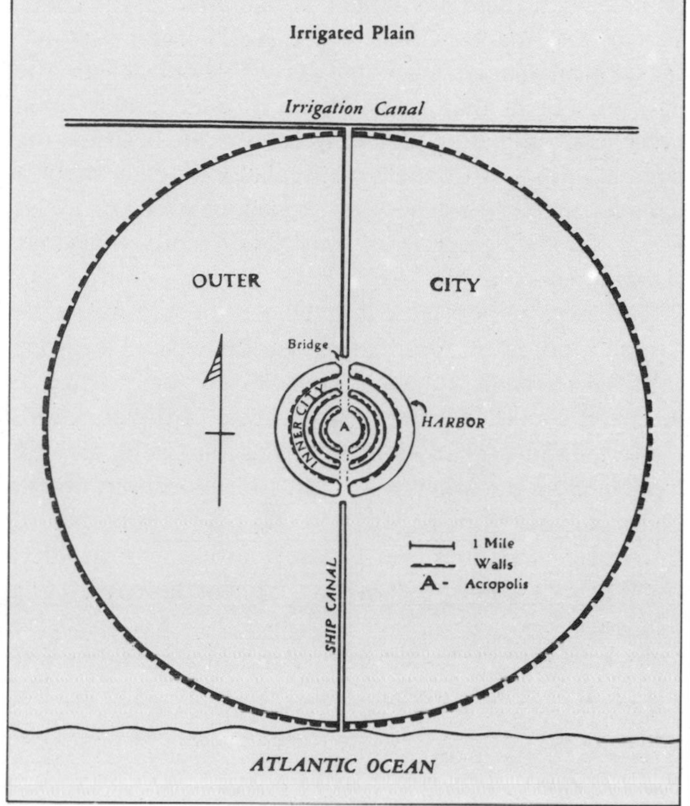

Stories about Atlantis date back to the *Critias* and *Timaeus* of Plato, who lived in the 4th century BC. In these works he put it into the mouths of his characters that Solon had been told by an Egyptian priest that a now-destroyed continent had once existed beyond the Pillars of Hercules (i.e., beyond the mouth of the Mediterranean). Ever since, legends about Atlantis have proliferated, at no time more than during the last century or so.

The 'modern revival' of Atlantology came about because of a remarkable book, published in 1882: *Atlantis, the Antediluvian World,* by the American writer and politician Ignatius Donnelly. Donnelly's work cannot be described as a ripping yarn: it is closely argued, and presents a plethora of

ABOVE: *A hypothetical map of the city of Atlantis, capital of the continent, based on the account in Plato's Critias.* **LEFT:** *Ignatius Donnelly's book, Atlantis the Antediluvian World (1882), was responsible for creating the modern 'cult' of Atlantology. This map shows his estimation of the continent's erstwhile position, based on deep-sea soundings. The ridges marked represent the Mid-Atlantic Ridge, which we now know to be an area where molten rock is emerging from beneath our planet's crust. This renders Donnelly's proposed siting dubious.*

evidence that there did indeed, at one time, exist a continent in the Atlantic Ocean. Zoological, geographical and sociological data are presented at considerable length. The only trouble is that such data are based purely upon hypotheses, and often further hypotheses are based on the original ones. Yet Donnelly's speculations clearly struck a popular chord, because even today new books about Atlantis are being published, each with a more outrageous central theory than the last.

The credulity of otherwise intelligent people cannot be stressed too much. A few years ago, I published a parody called *Sex Secrets of Ancient Atlantis*, and I was startled to receive a couple of letters from readers of the book who requested further information! Even the great are not immune from the Atlantology cult: the 19th-century British prime minister, William Gladstone, was at one stage moved to request funds from the Treasury so that an expedition could be sent to discover the lost continent (his request was refused).

So is there any reality behind the Atlantis legend? It seems that there probably is. In about 1400 BC the Mediterranean island of Thēra (now called Santorini) exploded, Krakatoa-fashion, annihilating the culture then residing on Thēra. More importantly, the tsunami resulting from the explosion seems to have destroyed the highly advanced Minoan civilization, based on the island of Crete. The loss of this culture was a significant event – certainly so far as the ancient world was concerned. Tales get better with the telling, and it seems reasonable to suggest that by Plato's time the lost land had become so huge, according to popular accounts, that it could no longer be 'fitted into' the Mediterranean. Hence, it must lie in the ocean beyond. (It seems likely that Plato used the tale of Atlantis solely for the sake of making philosophical points: there is no evidence that he actually believed it.)

UPPER RIGHT: *Artist's impression of the gardens of the royal palace in Atlantis*
LOWER RIGHT: *the royal banqueting hall*
BELOW: *the Palace of King Agamemnon*

The legend of Lemuria was born from the puzzlement of scientists during the 19th and early 20th centuries about the distribution of lemurs around the Indian Ocean. The first person to suggest that this could be explained in terms of a lost continent – that modern lemurs were the descendants of the lucky ones that had escaped to the shores of nearby land masses – seems to have been the British geologist Philip Lutley Sclater.

It is hard to agree with all of Sclater's ideas – one balks, for example, at his explanation of the suicidal habits of lemmings as an attempt to migrate from Europe to Atlantis – yet his suggestion that there might have been such a continent as Lemuria was at the time perfectly reasonable. Sadly, various occult groups, such as the Theosophists, latched onto the idea and produced various theories whose proofs had less than scientific rigour – for example, that Lemuria was originally populated 18 million years ago by Venusians, who lived there quite happily for a long while before accidentally discovering sex and thereby incurring the destruction of their continent.

The myth of Mu – often confused with Lemuria, because it, too, is supposed to have been in the Indian Ocean – has far less honourable origins. The myth was invented by Augustus Le Plongeon for a book called *Queen Moo and the Egyptian Sphynx*, published in 1896. The book purported to be based on ancient Mayan writings to which Le Plongeon was privy, although strangely enough copies were not available to other investigators. Colonel James Churchward 'took over' the legend of Mu: he published four books on the lost land during the 1920s and 1930s. His purpose was racist: he presented the case that the white races were superior to all others because they were more closely related to the superbeings who had inhabited Mu.

Have there been lost continents? In a sense, yes. The continents of our world have drifted about the face of the globe over the past few billion years, occasionally colliding to form temporary marriages and occasionally divorcing again. Their promiscuity can be explained in terms of the theory of plate tectonics. On occasion the continents have

TOP: *The submersion of Mu; 'Temples and palaces came crashing to the ground.' Or, at least, that was the story according to James Churchward in his book The Lost Continent of Mu (1931), from which this illustration has been taken.* **RIGHT:** *An illustration from Jules Verne's 20,000 Leagues Under the Sea, showing the French writer's view of the destruction of Atlantis.* **FAR RIGHT:** *'André Laurie' was the pseudonym of Paschal Grousset, a French communist novelist who collaborated on occasion with Verne. His version of Atlantis was, as one might expect, highly politicized.*

ANDRE LAURIE
ILLUSTRATIONS
DE GEORGE ROUX
ATLANTIS
LES ROMANS D'AVENTURES
COLLECTION HETZEL
BIBLIOTHÈQUE D'ÉDUCATION ET DE RÉCRÉATION
J. HETZEL ET Cie, 18, RUE JACOB, PARIS

come together to form 'supercontinents'. For example, several hundred million years ago all the continents came together to form a single land mass (now called Pangaea by geologists), which split up to form two supercontinents (Laurasia and Gondwanaland). These in turn split up.

Why is it reasonable to credit the one-time existence of continents such as Laurasia and Gondwanaland, but to reject Atlantis, Lemuria and Mu? The explanation is very simple. There is very good scientific evidence, from a diversity of disciplines, in support of Laurasia and Gondwanaland. There is none whatsoever in favour of Atlantis, Lemuria and Mu – unless the legend of Atlantis is genuinely a corruption of accounts of the destruction of the Minoan civilization.

Concerning Atlantis, there is one further suggestion. Our ancestors were far better navigators than we generally assume. Is it possible that they managed, several centuries before Christ, to reach the Americas? There they could have found various advanced cultures – now, alas, long gone because of the 'civilizing' efforts of the invading Europeans over the past few hundred years.

The discovery of, say, a Phoenician artefact in the Americas would cause something of a sensation in the archaeological world, but it would also destroy a mountain of Atlantological theses overnight.

LEFT: *A map of Atlantis taken from Athanasius Kircher's Mundus Subterraneous (1644). (By contrast with usual convention, north is at the bottom.) Kircher based his guess at the continent's position on Plato's accounts.* **TOP:** *A chart from the 1609 book La Navigation l'Inde Oriental, showing the islands of Brasil and Brandion.* **ABOVE:** *A chart made in 1634 by the French Geographer Royal showing the island of Brasil.*

The GREAT UNSOLVED MYSTERIES of SCIENCE

X
Z
D
H
O
C
H—C—OH
$CH_2OPO_3^{2}$

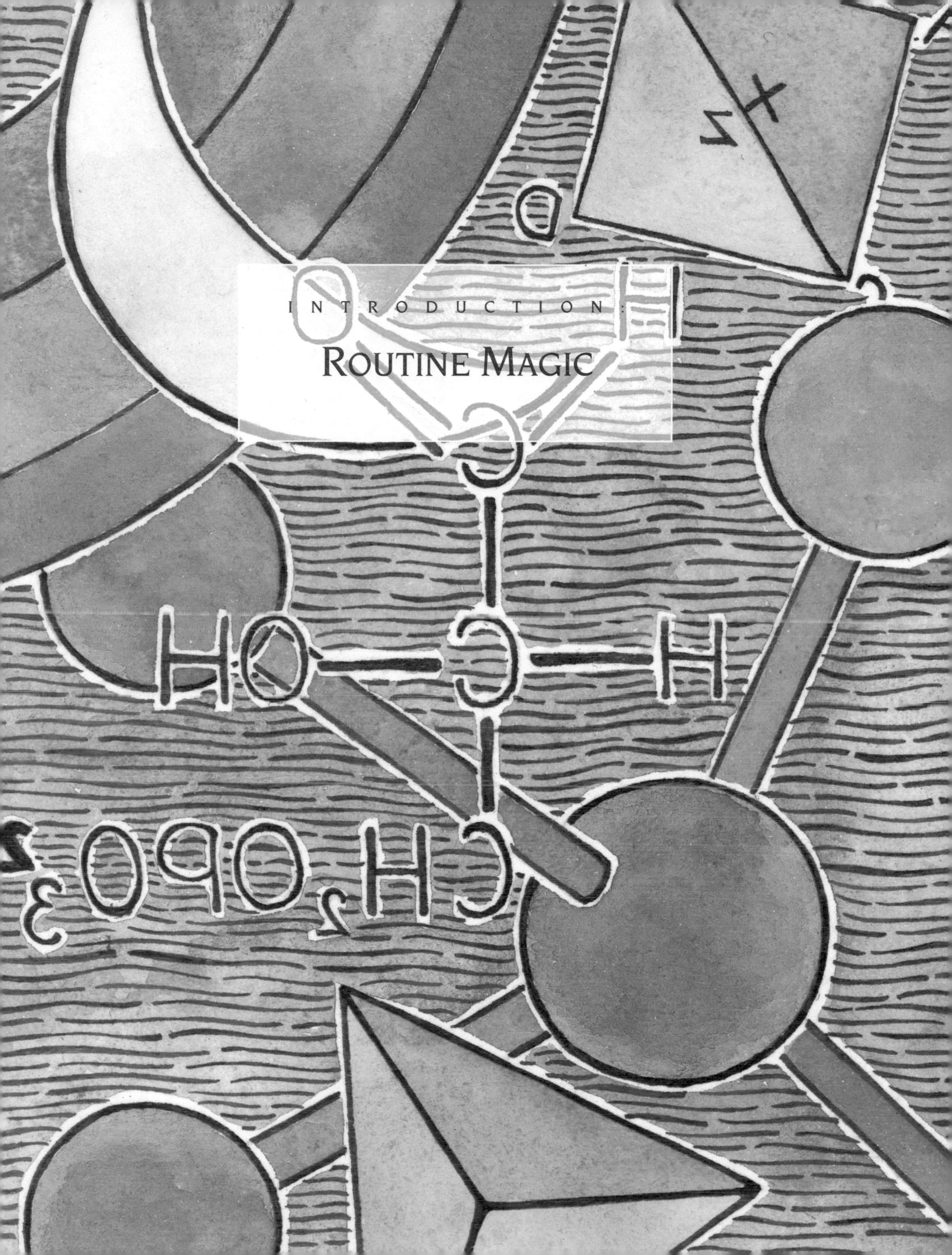

INTRODUCTION:

ROUTINE MAGIC

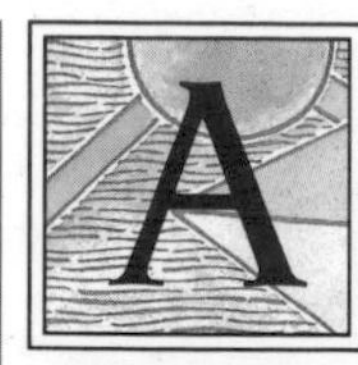

rthur C Clarke once remarked that any sufficiently advanced technology is, to the rest of us, indistinguishable from magic. To see the truth of this we need only look around us. For example, I am producing these words on a word-processor which shares my life for several hours each day. I know how to make it do all kinds of things – including a few that are not in the manufacturer's manual – but I have not the first idea as to how it actually works. To me, the whole process might just as well be magic.

Science is a form of magic, too – indeed, scientists at NASA, when performing yet another theoretically impossible feat, commonly refer to it as 'routine magic'. So I make no apologies for beginning Part 2 in the way that a conjurer might, by giving you an apparently free choice from the pack while in fact forcing on you the particular card that I want you to take.

Pick a mathematical equation – any equation. What a surprise! You happen to have chosen this one:

$$x^n + y^n = z^n$$

Now this is a very interesting equation indeed. If x, y, z and n all represent whole numbers, it appears that the equation is an impossible one for any value of n greater than 2. The word 'appears' is used advisedly because, although computers have been used to show that the equation does not work for values of n up to several thousand, no one has yet been able to prove for certain that there is *no* number n greater than 2 for which suitable values of x, y and z cannot be slotted in to produce a valid equation.

This is something of a mystery – but there is a greater mystery involved. The Frenchman Pierre de Fermat (1601–65) was one of the greatest mathematicians ever to have lived: his contributions are too many to mention. Unfortunately, he was interested in mathematics only as a hobby, and so he did not bother to publish any of his work. (It first became known to the wider world when, five years after Fermat's death, his son published his notes.)

LEFT *Home computers were unheard-of only a couple of decades ago; now they have become 'routine magic'.*

One day Fermat was reading a book on mathematics when he had an inspiration. Hastily he scribbled in the margin,

> WHERE n IS A NUMBER LARGER THAN 2, THERE ARE NO WHOLE NUMBERS x, y, z SUCH THAT $x^n + y^n = z^n$, AND OF THIS I HAVE FOUND A MOST MARVELLOUS PROOF, BUT THIS MARGIN IS TOO SMALL TO CONTAIN IT.

And that is precisely *all* we have of what has now come to be known as Fermat's Last Theorem. We can discount the possibility that Fermat was lying: this was a personal note, for him alone to read. It is of course possible that he was wrong in his initial assumption – which would explain why he never expanded his 'proof' in his notes – but we have to remember that the man was a mathematical genius. For more than three centuries mathematicians have struggled to rediscover Fermat's Last Theorem, but without success. The matter is still a mystery.

Many of the mysteries of science are more important than Fermat's Last Theorem. Or are they? Even the most seemingly trivial gap in our knowledge or understanding can represent some very major failure in our comprehension – it can mean that our overall ideas are seriously wrong. This was shown dramatically in the early years of this century.

The planet Mercury orbits the Sun more closely than do any of the others. It is a small, rocky body; its surface is covered with craters and blistered by the heat of the Sun. Like the other planets it travels around the Sun in an ellipse, which means that at some times it is closer to the Sun than at others. The point of closest approach is called the *perihelion* of a planet.

All of this seemed to be well understood until early this century, because it was explained in terms of Newton's theory of gravitation. There was only one fly in the ointment – but it was the smallest, most insignificant of flies.

Mercury's perihelion *advanced* a little more than the theory said it ought to. This was discovered in about 1840 by the French astronomer Urbain Leverrier (1811–77).

When we draw a picture of a planet's orbit we show the Sun, of course, and a single line around it in the shape of an ellipse. (Imagine a 'squashed circle' with the Sun just off-centre.) However, the truth is not quite as simple as this, because the planet does not exactly retrace its path each time it goes around the Sun. Instead, the orbit as a whole twists a little further round each time, so that a true drawing of the planet's course should really look more like one of the patterns produced by a children's Spirograph toy. The net effect is that, each time, the perihelion is a little further round than the last time – or, to put it another way, the perihelion advances. We *now* know this to be true of all the planets; however, the effect is so small that only in the case of Mercury was it detectable by nineteenth-century astronomers. And even with Mercury the change involved is minuscule: it is, in terms of angles, about 40 seconds per century (there are 3600 seconds in each degree of arc).

ABOVE *Pierre de Fermat, the mathematical genius who left us with one of science's greatest conundra.*

For several decades most scientists assumed that the discrepancy was too negligible to worry about: after all, no one said that everything in the Universe should work perfectly. Others did worry, though, and agreed with Leverrier that there must be a planet even closer to the Sun than Mercury; the gravitational tug of this hypothetical planet – which Leverrier christened Vulcan – could cause the anomalous advance of Mercury's perihelion. Astronomers made strenuous efforts to observe Vulcan, generally attributing their lack of success to the fact that a small body so close to the Sun would be incredibly difficult to detect. The whole affair seemed merely a minor mystery.

In fact it was a major mystery. Realization dawned only in 1915, when a comparatively young theoretical physicist called Albert Einstein published the paper that is now generally called the General Theory of Relativity. This theory, in passing, exactly accounted for the advance of Mercury's perihelion. More importantly, it rewrote large chunks of accepted science. Without Einstein's insight, in part inspired by the 'trivial' matter of Mercury's orbit, our knowledge of science, not to mention our technology, would be at a much lower level than it is today.

Apart from anything else, it is unlikely that anyone would have been able to develop the various forms of 'magic' that allow my word-processor to work.

Part 2 of this book brings together what I consider to be some of the major mysteries of science. Of course, in making my selection I am almost certainly falling into the same trap as those nineteenth-century scientists who thought that the anomalous orbit of Mercury was interesting but, in essence, a matter of little concern. At the same time, I can guarantee that some of the unsolved questions are very important indeed. There could hardly be more fundamental mysteries than the reasons why the Universe came into existence, how life began on planet Earth, and so on. Other conundra may appear rather less 'cosmically' relevant; they may seem to be of little importance yet, like Mercury's orbit, may prove in the long term to be extremely important.

Perhaps arbitrarily, Part 2 is divided into three sections dealing, respectively, with mysteries from the past, mysteries of life, and mysteries of physics. The first section essentially

ABOVE *Stan Gooch, the author of* Cities of Dreams.
RIGHT *Religion can be regarded as a primitive attempt to explain scientifically all the phenomena around us.* This Sri Lankan *Buddhist priest confronts an image of the Buddha hoping to find, through contemplation, answers to the many mysteries humanity may never find the answer to.*

deals with the sciences of geology and archaeology; the second with biology, sociology, psychology and anthropology; and the third with astronomy and physics. Of course, there is no real hard-and-fast barrier between these sciences: an advance in our understanding of physics can have profound effects on our understanding of biology, and so on. This interrelation of various disciplines is fundamental to science: the word 'science' itself derives from a Latin word meaning 'knowledge' – a term that embraces far more than the circumscribed disciplines just mentioned. It seems to be part of human nature, however, to seek to categorize things, and the various aspects of what is in essence a single, broadbased quest for further knowledge and understanding have not been spared.

Here, too, we have a mystery; this time a psychological one, or perhaps it is really the province of anthropology, or archaeology, or ... Why is it that we human beings are so *curious* about everything? Why is it that we should want to know things that are, in the broad scheme, totally irrelevant? You yourself are an example of this phenomenon at work, through the simple fact that you are reading this book. Could you not equally have said: 'Ha! Mysteries of science! Leave 'em to the scientists!'

Yet even people with severe mental retardation show a high level of curiosity in certain circumstances. As do higher-order animals, as anyone who lives with a cat or a dog will confirm. As do – but surely I cannot mean it! – lugworms. Lugworms are among the least intellectually blessed of all God's creatures, yet experiments have shown that they can (at least apparently) become bored, and the corollary of boredom is surely curiosity. This would suggest that curiosity is not a by-product of intelligence, as we might expect, but rather an essential property of life. Alternatively, it may be a prerequisite for the evolutionary development of intelligence – which leads us to the premonition that, in a few billion years' time, there may be intelligent lugworms stalking the Earth. The idea hardly bears thinking about.

Or perhaps it does. Chimpanzees are very intelligent – for animals. They have a highly developed sense of curiosity. Over the past few decades researchers have shown that chimps can create artworks (abstract thought), use tools in a quite sophisticated fashion, and understand the concept of language: humans and chimps can use sign languages like Ameslan to communicate with each other to a reasonably advanced level. (Interestingly, the chimps are able to manipulate the language to such an extent that they can create new words and phrases.) For all of these reasons, it hardly seems to offend rationality to assume that, over millennia or billennia, chimps will evolve to become as intelligent as we are now.

The lugworms may be lagging a long way behind, but perhaps their time may come?

Curiosity is a prime example of a mystery of science. It has particular interest in that we all know what the word means and yet none of us know what curiosity actually *is*. We recognize it when we come across it. The same is true, for that matter, of the phenomenon of intelligence – for which no one has as yet been able to produce an adequate definition.

We can assume – indeed, we *have* to assume – that our primitive forebears had a strong sense of curiosity. It is likely that some at least of nature's experiments as it sought to produce *Homo sapiens* were as intelligent as us, even though their type of intelligence may have been very different. (As an aside, Stan Gooch, in his 1989 book *Cities of Dreams*, presents the idea that Neanderthal Man – or, in his context, Neanderthal Woman – created a civilization as complex as ours but based on thoughts rather than on artefacts. His theory is controversial, to put it mildly; but at the very least he portrays the kind of different, 'alien' intelligence our ancestors may have had.) Those people of prehistory differed from us in one important respect: they did not possess the huge databank of past discoveries which we do. For example, if no one has yet discovered the principle of the lens, it is difficult to invent the telescope; if you want to erect an astronomical observatory, therefore, you have to do your best with the current technology – in other words, build Stonehenge or some similar megalithic monument. Your reasons for this colossal exploitation of what is to you hi-tech may be quite divorced from ours (*we* want to look for black holes, whereas *you* want to ascertain the precise time you should sacrifice a virgin in order to propitiate the gods), but the principle is much the same. You have, like it or not, curiosity and with it an adjunct: the desire to *explain* things. But perhaps these explanations may be a little bit too versatile for modern tastes:

- Why was there an eclipse? – The gods did it.
- Why did our village catch fire? – The gods did it.
- Why have we been flooded? – The gods did it.
- Why do I exist? – The gods did it.
- What will happen to me after I die? – It is in the lap of the gods.

Nevertheless, the very fact that an explanation should have been created at all tells us quite a lot about the way that the human mind works. The urge to explain seems to be part of the whole process that involves also the phenomena of curiosity and intelligence. This is why all those scientists have given so much time and effort to such apparent trivia as Fermat's Last Theorem and the advance of Mercury's perihelion. It seems that as a species, we can never be content until we have an explanation for *everything*.

Clearly there are many benefits to this urge. However, there is a negative side. Once an explanation – any explanation – has been produced, people tend to stick with it, no matter how much evidence thereafter appears to contradict it. This tends to happen at several levels. Our hypothetical cavedwellers with their universal explanation that 'the gods

did it' are not too far separated from the modern Westerner who believes that the Soviet Union is an unalleviatedly 'evil empire' or that Blacks are inferior to Whites: all three explanations are easy to take on board, they are much simpler than the arguments put forward by the people who disagree with them, and, once accepted, they are clung to with a limpet-like grip.

Of course, people who have such simplistic ideas are never 'us'; they are always 'someone else'. They are the unfortunate primitives or fools: *we* know much better than that!

Do we? Most readers of this book aged over 30 will have been taught at school that the atom is made up of little billiard balls: in the centre there is the nucleus, made of biggish billiard balls called protons and neutrons; around the nucleus travel very small billiard balls called electrons. In fact, the atom is nothing like this (for example, electrons

BELOW *In a small Zimbabwean church built of straw a minister of God attempts to unravel the mysteries of the cosmos for the benefit of his congregation of women and children. Humanity has an intense desire to explain reality, and uses religion as a means of doing so.*

RIGHT *A Tunisian Rabbi seeks the answer to universal questions in a copy of the Bible.*

are likely to be nothing more than 'confluences of probability waves' – in other words, totally incomprehensible in everyday terms), yet what do *you* think of when you think of an atom? Almost certainly, the image in your mind's eye involves those billiard balls you learned about at school.

The same sort of thing, sadly, goes on at a higher level. Once an explanation has been accepted by the scientific community as a whole, it is very hard to dislodge it. The scientific establishment can resist a new idea with such complacent zeal that even Joshua with his trumpets would have no effect. Of course, in many cases this rigidity is perfectly justified – the notion that the Moon is in fact a vast spaceship placed in Earth-orbit millions of years ago by visiting extraterrestrials has, shall we say, little in its favour. But in other instances the rejection of anything new and the fixed-minded adherence to the old can lock science into a state of long-term moribundity. For centuries it was ordained that, despite the evidence, everything in the Universe circled the Earth: a number of people were put to death because they happened to disagree. During the nineteenth century it was *de rigueur* to think that the Universe was filled with a sort of stuff called the luminiferous aether: disagree with that notion and you could say farewell to your hopes of a professorship. For decades during the twentieth century it was heresy to give any credit to the ideas of Alfred Wegener (1880-1930), and others before him, that the continents slowly moved in different directions over the surface of the globe. All of these ideas – and there are countless other examples – have advanced the course of science considerbly: who knows where our science and scientific theory would be now had not the monolith of scientific orthodoxy stood for so long in their way?

To be fair to the scientific establishment, we have to recognize that the vast majority of outrageous new theories are rubbish from start to finish. Typically they come from people whose acquaintanceship with the sciences is minimal but whose fabulous new theory will revolutionize the whole of science. (One massive tome, purporting to change our ideas of the Universe, listed in its bibliography a single work on astronomy – a children's book.) Yet we cannot help but feel that perhaps the establishment should be just a little bit less obdurate when confronted by new ideas. Some people still do not accept Einstein's Relativity; many others refuse

ABOVE *The Italian astronomer Galileo Galilei (1564–1642), who got into trouble with the Roman Catholic Church because he stated in public that, as a result of his observations, he had come to the conclusion that the Earth was not the centre of the Universe.*

to accept that Relativity may not be the *final* explanation (even though such an acquiescence to received ideas would have horrified Einstein himself).

So: we have curiosity, intelligence and the impetus to find explanations for things. Once we have found an explanation that seems to make sense we tend to cling to it religiously. This is true in all cultures, whatever their level of sophistication. That this curiosity (the urge to discover new things) should act in tandem with its apparent opposite, conservatism of thought, within the human animal is an obvious paradox – another mystery.

I shall now ask you again to abandon your conservatism and allow your curiosity full rein. The words 'probably', 'likely' and 'unlikely' litter the text, even when I am talking about

ABOVE *The changing shape of the world map as a result of plate movements. In geological terms 30 million years is not a very long time, which is why the change is so minimal.* **TOP RIGHT** *A schematic representation of the interaction of the world's plates. New material is contributed to the Earth's crust at midocean ridges. At the other edge of the plate, material is either subducted back down into the mantle (the subcrustal layer of the Earth) or collides with the edge material of another plate to build up a mountain range.*

RIGHT *Diagram of the San Andreas Fault, a plate margin whose rumblings have claimed many lives in San Francisco in the earthquakes of 1906 and 1989.*

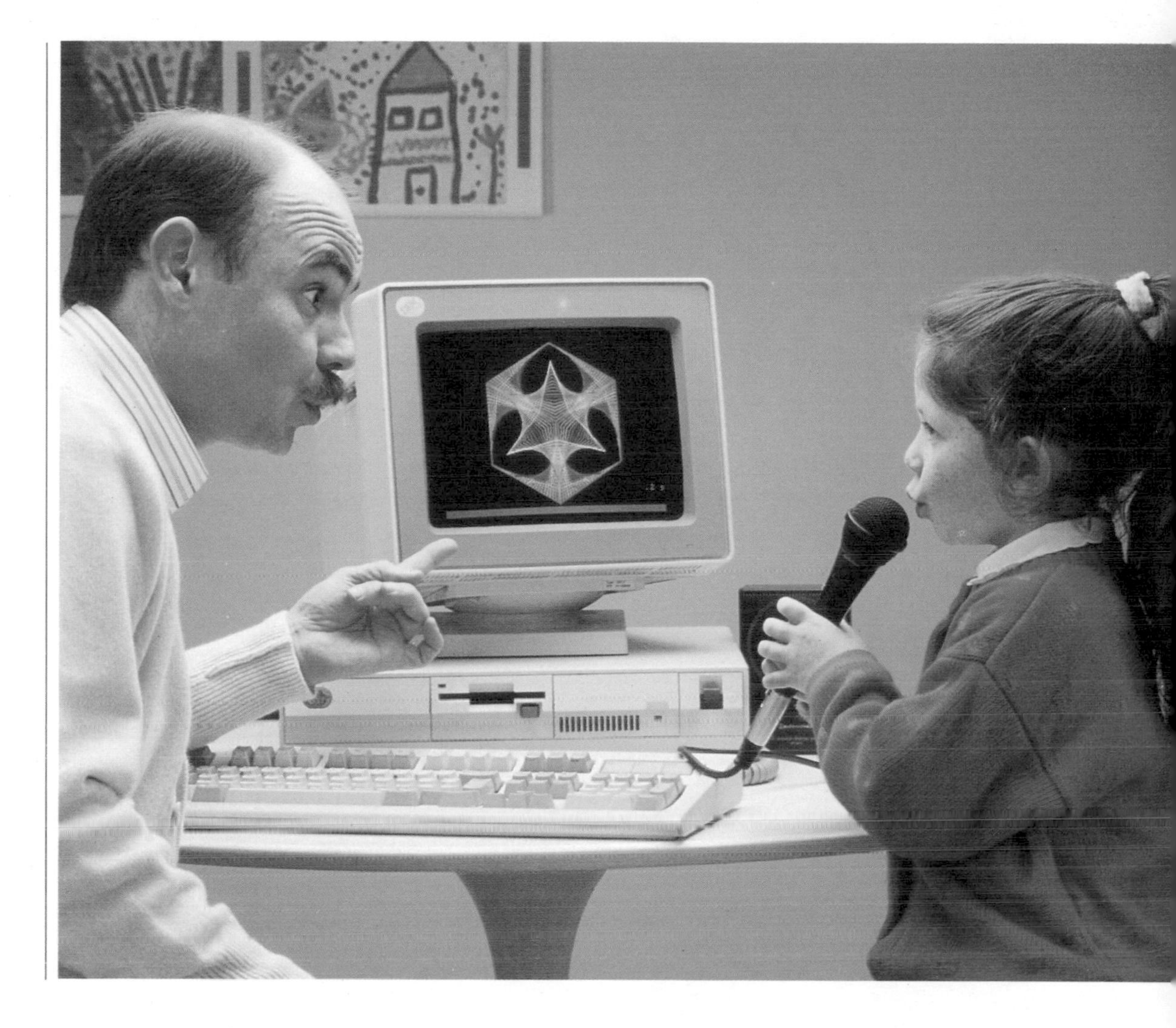

RIGHT *It's all just 'routine magic' to the little girl whose words spoken into the microphone call up a coloured image on screen. Adults, however, have greater difficulty in accommodating their views to the 'miracles' of modern technology.*

what is widely regarded as fact. Some of the ideas which I discuss are currently rated 'improbable', but should not be dismissed for that reason alone: their supporters may be in a minority, but that minority is often a very distinguished one.

A final note. People often treat science as if it were some sort of 'forbidden country'. In fact, one of the perennial irritations of those involved in the sciences is that it is somehow chic to be innumerate and totally ignorant of physics, mathematics and the rest, but at the same time taboo to be ignorant of the basics of, say, literature. This is not helped by an educational system and a cultural climate which often present science in a negative way – as either boring or difficult (or both).

In fact, the essential concepts of science are very often neither. I am aware, though, that when some readers first open this book they may find a few of the ideas discussed superficially intimidating. I would advise such readers not to lose heart: there is nothing in this book which cannot be grasped by an 11-year-old who employs a little application: I know, because I've tested it on an 11-year-old.

Part 2 could have been many times its current length had I explained everything in detail. In other words, in order to get across a general point I have often simplified the argument. I must ask those who are more familiar with the sciences to forgive me for any passages where they feel I might be guilty of *over*simplification. I would guide such readers to the Bibliography section at the end of the book.

The use of the word 'unsolved' about any aspect of science implies that, somewhere, a solution awaits us. That is the glorious challenge of science.

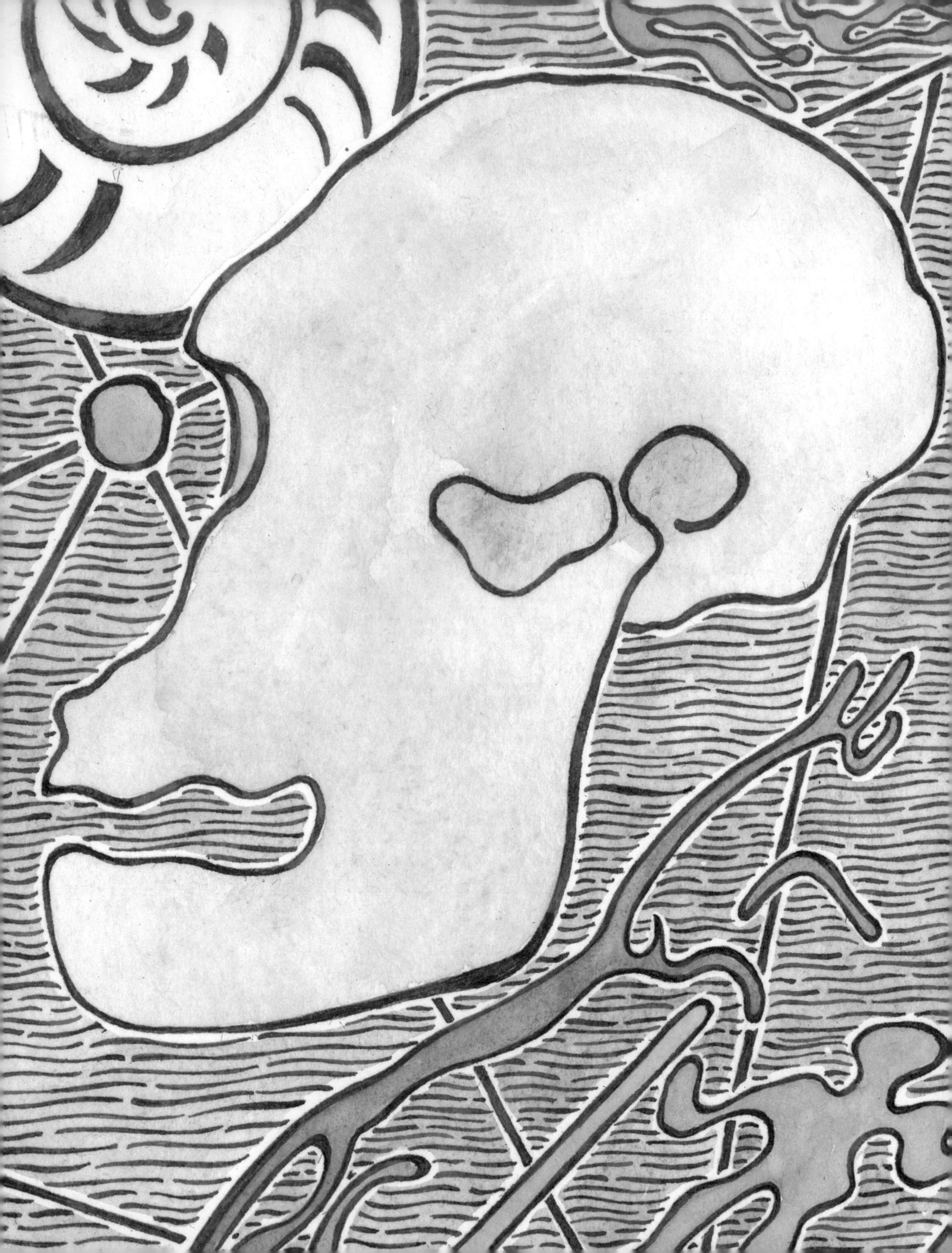

PART ONE

MYSTERIES FROM THE PAST

As LP Hartley remarked in his classic novel *The Go-Between* (1953), 'the past is a foreign country: they do things differently there' Hartley was not, of course, referring to prehistory – except perhaps the prehistory of the individual soul – but his remark sums up our dilemma. When scientists attempt to unravel the mysteries of the past they always run up against a brick wall. They can take artefacts, fragments of bone, curious edifices and so on, and make inferences from these, but they know that they can never, ever state precisely the truth of the past. Perhaps if someone invented a time machine (almost certainly a scientific impossibility) archaeologists would have the satisfaction of being able to prove and disprove each other's theories; failing that, we have to accept that the science of the distant past is a matter of informed deduction and, let us face it, guesswork.

That this is the case is exemplified by several works of fantasy and science fiction. In more than one story Clifford Simak put forward the notion that the flesh-tones of dinosaurs might have been iridescent, rather than the drab grey-greens and browns depicted in so many artists' impressions. Of course, Simak was not putting this forward as a serious theory. He was simply pointing out that palaeontology, as a science, depends on the interpretation of fossil relics of bones, not flesh; no palaeontologist has any clue as to what a living dinosaur actually looked like. A similar point was made by the eminent US naturalist Stephen Jay Gould in his introduction to Bjørn Kurtén's fascinating novel *Dance of the Tiger* (1980), whose focus is the hypothetical extermination of

LEFT *Our ideas of the appearance of our prehistoric ancestors change according to current social attitudes. Life may indeed have been nasty, brutal and short a few hundred thousand years ago, but there are those who claim that at least the shortness was a benefit in comparison with modern human existence. The truth is that we do not even know what our ancestors actually looked like.*

Neanderthals by Cro-Magnons, about 35,000 years ago. Gould remarks:

> ... I FELT ENLIGHTENED – AND EMBARRASSED. KURTÉN DEPICTS NEANDERTHALS AS WHITE-SKINNED, CRO-MAGNONS AS DARK. UNTIL READING THIS, I HAD NEVER REALIZED THAT MY UNQUESTIONED PICTURE OF NEANDERTHALS AS DARK AROSE FROM STANDARD RECONSTRUCTIONS ... AND FROM THE RACISM THAT SADLY AFFLICTS US ALL AND LEADS WHITE PEOPLE TO ASSOCIATE INFERIORITY AND DARKNESS. KURTÉN'S RECONSTRUCTION MAKES MORE SENSE, SINCE NEANDERTHALS LIVED IN GLACIAL ENVIRONMENTS AND LIGHT SKIN MAY BE AN ADAPTATION TO LIFE IN MIDDLE TO HIGH LATITUDES. YET ANY SCIENTIST WOULD BE RIGHTLY DUBBED A FOOL IF HE PUBLISHED A PROFESSIONAL PAPER ON 'THE SKIN COLOUR OF NEANDERTHAL DEDUCED FROM GENERAL EVOLUTIONARY PRINCIPLES'.

The complement of Gould's last comment is likewise true: any scientist who claimed that the Neanderthals were dark-skinned would clearly be committing an act of intellectual folly. The stark fact is that, as with the dinosaurs, we simply do not know what Neanderthal and Cro-Magnon people actually *looked* like. We know their average heights, but we do not know if our ancestors were hairy or smooth, blue-eyed or brown-eyed, loquacious or capable of communicating only the most fundamental of information in grunts. We do not know if their society (and here, of course, we are assuming that they actually *had* a society) was matriarchal or patriarchal. We do not know if they had music or even if they had genuine art: cave-paintings and bone-carvings might be manifestations of the muse, but they could equally well have been executed solely for mystical purposes.

In this section we shall look at some scientific mysteries that are rather more profound than the skin-colours of dinosaurs or prehistoric human beings. Instead, let us start with a fairly fundamental question ...

How Did Life Begin?

You may not seem to have much in common with your cat or with the bacterium living in your gut, but in fact, in terms of basic biology, there is little to choose between you. Your biochemistry is almost identical. The molecules of your body, because of the way they are made up, possess the ability to rotate polarized light in a leftward direction. This is characteristic of life on Earth – if and when we discover lifeforms on other planets, there is a 50 percent chance that their molecules, unlike ours, may rotate polarized light to the right. You, the cat and the bacterium also share the feature that your body is made up of cells, the boundary between one cell and the next consisting of a very definite barrier called a membrane.

Just in case you were thinking that there was nevertheless a basic difference between you and that bacterium (not to mention the cat), there are two types of important complicated molecules shared by all of our planet's lifeforms: nucleic acids and proteins.

For these reasons it seems reasonable to suggest that all lifeforms on Earth shared a common origin: there is little likelihood that it sprang up contemporaneously in several different parts of the globe. However, there is something of a mystery as to what caused that origin.

One idea that has been suggested is that the precursors of life – complex organic molecules – arrived here from outer space. Supporters of such hypotheses fall into three main camps. First there are those theorists, notably Fred Hoyle and Chandra Wickramasinghe, who propose that the interiors of comets are much more likely sites for the formation of organic chemicals than the surfaces of planets. It is almost certain that, during the Earth's early history, the planet was a frequent victim of cometary impacts. When this happened, say Hoyle and Wickramasinghe, the organic molecules within the comets were spewed out over the land. Further chemical reactions led to living organisms.

A second idea is known as the 'bootstraps' theory. The proposition is that, some billions of years ago, visiting extraterrestrials arrived in their spaceship to view the Earth. In one way or another they 'infected' the youthful planet with living organisms – perhaps, before their departure, they emptied out their chemical toilets, leaving a thriving population of bacteria. Of course, there are two basic problems here:

- there is no possible proof of the hypothesis
- the hypothesis may seem to give a palatable explanation of the emergence of life on Earth, but it merely pushes the problem one stage back: how did life originate on the planet of these putative alien space travellers?

A third possibility connected with the idea that life on Earth originated from space is manifestly a nonsense – except for the fact that some remarkably distinguished scientists have supported it, the most recent of them being Francis Crick, winner with James Watson and Maurice Wilkins of the 1962 Nobel Prize in Physiology or Medicine for their work in unravelling the structure of DNA, the 'double helix'. In his 1981 book *Life Itself* Crick suggests that life came to our world because a billennia-old extraterrestrial civilization deliberately sent out vast numbers of spacecraft packed with living spores, hoping thereby to 'seed' countless potentially life-

ABOVE *A knotted wrack of algae. The algae are among the simplest of plants and appeared very early in the history of life on Earth.*
RIGHT *The volcanic island Surtsey, off Iceland, emerged from the sea in 1964. Volcanic eruptions like this one probably assisted the development of life on our planet.*

supporting planets in the Galaxy. This theory is, of course, subject to the two criticisms mentioned above. However, it is worth a little further attention because it is a recent example of a whole group of theories that come under the umbrella heading of *panspermia*. (Both the Hoyle/Wickramasinghe proposal and the 'bootstraps' theory can likewise be considered as variants of the panspermic hypothesis.)

The word 'panspermia' in itself gives the clue to the common element in this group of theories. The Greek prefix *pan* means 'all'; the *spermia* part of the word comes from the Greek for 'seed'. 'Panspermia', as a word, therefore refers to those theories which insist that life came to Earth because 'spores' were somehow blasted off into space in the hope that they might eventually encounter a life-supporting planet – like Earth.

The first panspermic hypothesis can be traced back to 1743 and Benôit de Maillet, who suggested that the germs of life came to Earth from space; they fell into the oceans and in due course grew into fish and, later, amphibians, reptiles and mammals. Much later, in 1908, the first rigorous formulation of the panspermic hypothesis appeared: this was produced by the Swedish chemist Svante Arrhenius (1859–1927). According to Arrhenius, the Universe was packed with 'proto-life' spores that drifted between the stars, their interstellar voyages powered by the radiation-pressure of light.

At the time, the proposal was plausible although, of course, it still ducked the issue of where the spores had come from in the first place. Bacterial spores can withstand extremes of hot and cold, not to mention the vacuum of space, for extended periods, germinating only when they attain more favourable environments. What Arrhenius did not know was that there is a large amount of X-radiation washing about in space, and to this his hypothetical spores would certainly have been vulnerable.

The trouble with all panspermic theories is that they look to outer space, yet we have no particular reason to believe that life could not have emerged right here on our own world. A further difficulty concerns the sheer numbers of such spores that would need to be involved. Imagine that we, the human species, released one billion living spores into the Universe, sending them off in random directions. By the time the spores reached the distance of the 'nearby' star α Centauri, 4.3 lightyears away, the spores would be about 13 million million million kilometres apart from each other.

Bearing in mind that the Earth is only about 150 million kilometres from the Sun, the chances of one of our spores being captured by any potentially life-sustaining planet of α Centauri can be seen to be very slender indeed. Of course, we could scatter many billions of spores, thereby reducing the odds, but even so the possibility of even one of them encountering a suitable receiving planet anywhere in the Universe is vanishingly small.

Here the Crick hypothesis has an advantage over the others, in that he proposes that those mysterious extraterrestrials did not simply scatter spores willy-nilly but sent out a computer-controlled spacecraft containing the spores as cargo. It is easy enough to programme a computer to direct spacecraft towards a long succession of likely stars, to carry out simple tests to establish whether any of the planets of those stars might be capable of sustaining life, and, when appropriate, to dump consignments of spores into the planet's atmosphere. Such a 'guided' enterprise – Crick calls the hypothesis 'Directed Panspermia' – would avoid the colossal wastage involved in a random scattering.

There is, however, a fundamental problem: motive. Interstellar spacecraft, and the computers to control them, do not come cheap. However advanced our hypothetical extraterrestrial civilization might be, building just one of these spacecraft would represent a significant investment. It might take millions of years before the spacecraft encountered a suitable planet, and billions before the result of its efforts would produce an intelligent lifeform, if at all. Taking all this into account, we have to ask why the extraterrestrials should be remotely interested in 'seeding' distant planets. To put it more simply, why should they bother?

Let us return to more conventional theories.

Our planet formed about 4.5–5 billion years ago. It should not be imagined, however, that the newborn Earth remotely resembled the world in which we live today. This was a very hot body, spewing its heat and gases copiously into space: it can be thought of as a planet-sized erupting volcano. In a comparatively short period – a few hundred million years or so – the Earth cooled down, and by this time, because of the gases belched out by its numerous volcanoes, it had an atmosphere. This atmosphere was not especially hospitable:

RIGHT *Eruption of Halemaumau, Hawaii, in 1961.*

LEFT *Eruption of Kilauea Iki, Hawaii, in 1959.* **BELOW** *Fountains of fire paint the sky in a 1973 eruption of Eldjfell, Iceland.* **RIGHT** *A NASA artist's impression of the surface of the planet Venus, a place which has frequently been described as the true-life equivalent of Hell. Volcanism on Venus might assist the development of life there were it not for the devastatingly high surface temperatures.*

most of its gases were extremely noxious. However, it is believed that in the virgin planet's oceans there evolved, by chance, complicated molecules called 'proteinoid globules' (or 'proteinoid microspheres'); alternatively, these molecules might have formed on the slopes of the primordial volcanoes and been washed, by rain, down to the seas. Various experiments done in volcanic environments have shown that proteinoid globules are very likely to form in such regions. Another possibility is that the globules could first have been created in the atmosphere by the electrical activity of thunderstorms. In all cases, it appears that the transition from 'complicated molecule' to life occurred in the oceans.

Protein molecules are the precursors of life. If you stir enough of them together and stand back for a few hundred million years, the result is likely to be a chemical entity capable of reproducing itself – one of the fundamental differences between living and nonliving material. This is what seems to have happened early in the history of the Earth, because the oldest known fossil remains of proteinoid globules are believed to date back about 4 billion years. The first living organism cannot have followed far behind.

If these theories are by and large correct we should expect to find proteinoid globules occurring spontaneously in modern volcanic environments. There is some evidence that this is indeed the case, but it is very scant. One reason might be that, as soon as a conglomeration of chemicals becomes complicated enough to become 'protolife', something comes along and eats it. This is not the flip comment it might seem. The notion is that, in countless regions of the world, life is at this very moment coming into existence – almost. We are the descendants of the first wave of life-formation; all others have been devoured by members of our 'generation'.

It is inherent in such ideas that life must be fairly common throughout the Universe. As yet we have no convincing evidence that this is the case.

We have talked loosely about the original atmosphere of the Earth, and the way in which it affected and perhaps still affects life. It is time to turn the tables and consider how the existence of life may have affected the atmosphere of the early Earth.

The primary gases emitted by active volcanoes are carbon dioxide, water vapour and compounds of nitrogen.

There is no reason to believe that this was not true also of the world's earliest volcanoes. Yet the Earth's atmosphere currently consists of about 78 percent nitrogen, 20 percent oxygen and 2 percent other gases. (The proportion of water vapour varies.) Something must have happened to convert the original stew of gases into the ones we breathe today.

According to current theories, all of this is entirely predictable, depending solely upon the distance the Earth is from the Sun. For the sake of comparison we can look at the planet Venus, which is much closer to the Sun than the Earth is, and the planet Mars, which is further away. From the very start the surface temperature on Venus must have been much hotter than that on Earth – purely because of the planet's proximity to the Sun. Most of the water vapour emerging from Venus's early volcanoes would therefore remain in the planet's atmosphere, in the form of clouds. The longer this persisted, the hotter the planet got, because energy from the Sun could penetrate down through the clouds but was incapable of escaping back out through them (the famous 'greenhouse effect'). In due course the surface temperature on Venus was higher than the boiling point of

terrestrial life. These, like plants do today, took carbon dioxide from the atmosphere, stripped away the carbon and emitted oxygen in return. We can date the 'oxygen revolution' – the time when oxygen became an important gas in the Earth's atmosphere – fairly precisely: it occurred about 410 million years ago. This can be deduced from the fact that rocks of this age are typically red: the iron in them rusted, a process which cannot occur without the presence of oxygen and water.

As yet, no one knows exactly how life originated on Earth. The possibilities seem almost endless. The seeds of life might have appeared spontaneously here or in space, or they might have been deliberately sent here by an extraterrestrial intelligence. The latter possibility is, to be polite, unlikely; the other two imply that life is very widespread throughout the Universe. If so, why is that we have not heard anything from all those other civilizations out there? We shall return to this question later.

LEFT *The surface of Mars as photographed in 1976 by Viking 2.*
BELOW *Old Red Sandstone*

water, so that there was no longer any possibility of liquid water on the planet's surface – in other words, there could be no rivers or seas. Mars, by contrast, being so much further away from the Sun, is very cold: the water vapour produced by its early volcanoes would swiftly have frozen solid, leaving a thin atmosphere composed largely of carbon dioxide. (There is evidence, though, that once upon a time Mars enjoyed running water.)

By contrast with both of these other planets, the Earth was just the right distance from the Sun. At its surface, water could exist as a liquid rather than as a gas, and so oceans and seas came into existence. Water is capable of dissolving carbon dioxide; the composition of the atmosphere would therefore change considerably. Nitrogen, on the other hand, is a very inert (nonreactive) gas: the quantities of it emerging from the volcanoes might have been, in percentage terms, extremely small, yet they stayed in the atmosphere.

However, so far as we are concerned the important constituent of the atmosphere is oxygen: without it we would never have come into existence. The clue to the plenitude of oxygen in the Earth's atmosphere would appear to be the respiratory activities of the lowest and earliest forms of

Why Did the Dinosaurs Disappear?

At the moment there is a single dominant species on our planet, *Homo sapiens* – in other words, you. But about 65 million years ago the picture was very different. The dominant animals were reptiles. Their size varied considerably, from behemoths like *Brontosaurus* to little scuttling beasts about the size of a hen.

The dinosaurs died out very suddenly. The reasons for this extinction are not well understood. It seems almost cer-

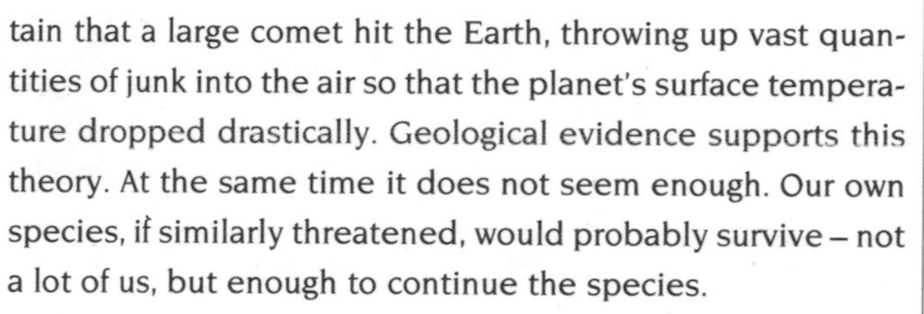

tain that a large comet hit the Earth, throwing up vast quantities of junk into the air so that the planet's surface temperature dropped drastically. Geological evidence supports this theory. At the same time it does not seem enough. Our own species, if similarly threatened, would probably survive – not a lot of us, but enough to continue the species.

For some reason the dinosaurs failed to survive: this is a considerable mystery. At the time of their demise the land

RIGHT *Skeleton of* Triceratops **BELOW** *Building on such skeletons, artists can come up with impressions of what dinosaurs like* Triceratops *looked like, but it should be stressed that such images are no more than guesses.*

LEFT *Barringer meteorite crater, between Flagstaff and Winslow, Arizona. The crater is about 1.280km across and about 175m deep.* FAR RIGHT *A fossil of Archaeopteryx, believed to be the ancestor of modern birds. Recently some scientists, including Professor Sir Fred Hoyle, have claimed that these fossils are forgeries.* BELOW RIGHT *A large female crocodile on the Nile River. Why the crocodiles should have survived the extinction of dinosaurs is a mystery.*

was infested by the mammal-like reptiles, which had the looks and probably the habits of rats: we are the descendants of such creatures. One current explanation as to why the dinosaurs died and the mammal-like reptiles survived is that the dinosaurs were cold-blooded: when conditions became arctic, the dinosaurs just died. Modern theories, however, suggest that the dinosaurs were warm-blooded, like the mammals (including ourselves) that currently dominate the Earth. When the dinosaurs died, why did the mammal-like reptiles not do likewise?

The short answer to that question is that nobody knows. As noted, it seems very likely that, 65 million years ago, a comet did indeed hit the Earth. The impact threw up vast quantities of material into the upper atmosphere, where it stayed for months or years, blotting out the light of the Sun; some of this material came from the comet, some from the surface of the Earth. The net result was that much of the energy from the Sun was reflected back out into space, so that the surface of the Earth became much cooler than it had been before. Also, without sunlight, plants cannot photosynthesize, so there must have been a very considerable food shortage. In fact, the effect on all forms of life may well have been as devastating as the 'nuclear winter' which will occur should the nations of Earth ever engage in a nuclear war. To extend the parallel, the impact of the comet would also have released large quantities of hard radiation.

In a certain way, of course, the dinosaurs were not really exterminated: we see their descendants all around us, in the form of modern reptiles and birds. Looked at from this angle, the mystery may not be such a mystery after all. We can imagine the following series of events:

- animal life evolved until the reptiles dominated all other forms
- the impact of the comet obliterated large portions of the Animal Kingdom, with mammals suffering just as severe depredations as the reptiles (fishes and other marine animals probably came out of it all comparatively lightly)
- second time around, by chance or otherwise, as animals further evolved to repopulate the Earth, the mammals came out on top (although a case can be made that it was really the insects that came out on top!)

A further clue could be the sheer size of the dinosaurs. When there is a severe food shortage, the first to suffer are the larger animals. The giant herbivorous dinosaurs would have been the first to go, as plant matter became scarce, but they would soon be followed by the large carnivores that had preyed upon them. Naturally, these predators must have turned their attentions to other animals, like the mammal-like reptiles; but we must remember that these animals were *small*. To keep a *Tyrannosaurus rex* alive would require catching and killing a tremendous number of mammal-like reptiles. Add to the beast's problems that it was already enfeebled by lack of nutrition, and one can see that its chances of survival were really pretty low. In other words, when the disaster came, it was the big animals that were most vulnerable, and at the time the big animals were all, as it happened, dinosaurs.

We can note in this context that the big animals of today, the whale and the elephant, are quite recent arrivals. The earliest known elephants date from about 50 million years ago – well after the event – and were then only about the size of a pig. The earliest known whales date from about the same time, but in this case the situation is slightly more complicated, in that these early whales were very similar to modern ones, and could be big – up to 15m (50ft) long. By comparison, *Diplodocus*, the biggest of the dinosaurs, was typically 28m (91ft) long, while a modern blue whale can reach a length of about 30m (100ft). Nevertheless, a 15m (50ft) animal is no mean beast; moreover, because of the way that the earliest known whales so closely resemble modern ones, we have to assume that their ancestry stretched back some way, even though no relevant fossils have yet been discovered. Since 15 million years is a very short period in terms of evolution, we have to conclude that there were some big whales around at the time of the catastrophe. However, as noted in passing in the case of fishes, conditions in the oceans are likely to have been less drastically affected than those on land.

Another puzzle is that one kind of large reptile survived – the crocodiles. Some of these animals were and are big: one species which existed around the time of the catastrophe was 15m (50ft) long. Of course, these animals are semi-aquatic, but much of their prey is terrestrial. One can only assume that, at least for a while, they were able to survive on fully aquatic prey, such as fishes. Besides, there is good evidence that the crocodiles of that time were much faster-moving reptiles than their dinosaur contemporaries – indeed, the ancestors of modern crocodiles may have been nimble land-animals, since to this day crocodiles have an ankle structure typical of a rapid terrestrial carnivore. Perhaps the crocodiles, through their speed, were able to kill sufficient numbers of smaller animals to survive the 'winter'. More likely, they sustained themselves by a mixture of both strategems.

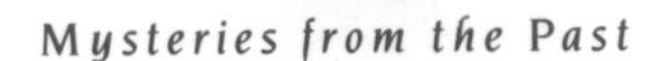

Did the Neanderthals Have an Advanced Civilization?

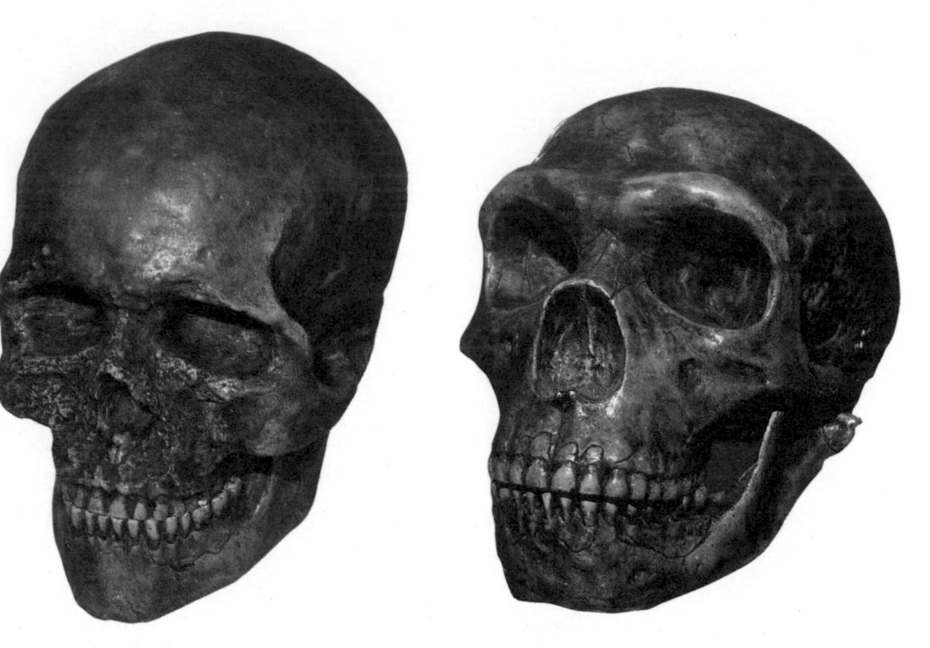

FAR LEFT *Reconstruction of a Cro-Magnon skull.* **LEFT** *Reconstruction of a Neanderthal skull.* **FAR RIGHT** *Dugout canoes in Nepal. Such craft have been in use since humanity's very earliest days; they are an example of an invention which serves its purpose so well that there is little need to improve upon it.*

The idea of any form of prehistoric human beings having a civilization that we could reasonably described as 'advanced' seems to be a contradiction in terms. After all, one aspect of civilization is the development of a written means of communication, which implies that records are preserved. When this happens, there is no longer any such thing as prehistory: it has been replaced by history.

However, it has been pointed out – most recently by Stan Gooch in his *Cities of Dreams* (1989) – that this is to take a rather narrow view of what we mean by civilization. Because of our own cultural heritage, we think in terms of things like the construction of permanent artefacts and the invention of useful tools like writing and mathematics – in other words we are, essentially, technologically oriented. But is this the only way in which a complicated and highly structured civilization can evolve?

The answer has to be a resounding 'no'. We can legitimately think of an ants' nest as a civilization: its members carry out highly specific or even very generalized tasks in pursuit of the common good. Yet ants have yet to develop writing, and their major artefacts – their nests – can be demolished in minutes using a spade. Dolphins are highly intelligent beings (they may be as intelligent as we are, and perhaps even more so), yet they have no writing and create no artefacts. Nevertheless, in many dolphin communities the interactions between the various members are commonly more civilized than those current in parts of our cities. There are even human communities around the world which exist without such tools as writing, while constructing artefacts, commonly of wood, that cannot be described as permanent (in terms of thousands or millions of years).

Ants can create a structured society without being possessed, individually, of very much by way of brain. Bees do much the same. One can look at other animals – baboons, chimps and so on – and see a lesser form of the same structure being created. Inevitably we have to conclude that social action, commonly considered a by-product of intelligence, can in fact exist quite independently of that quality.

Neanderthals possessed bigger brains than we do; the Cro-Magnons, generally regarded as having wiped out the Neanderthal precursors, were similarly large-brained. This is not proof in itself that our ancestors were more intelligent than we are: it seems that the ability of a brain depends less on its size than on the extent of its complexity, as epitomized by the degree of crenulation (folding) on its exterior. Unfortunately, since the brains of dead people rot swiftly, we have little notion of the degree of crenulation of the Neanderthal or Cro-Magnon brain.

It is therefore plausible that Neanderthals enjoyed a civilization which, while very different from our own, had its own structures, conventions and complexities. Gooch, in *Cities of Dreams*, postulates a society based on what we can call 'mental artefacts'; that is, ideas rather than physical constructions. The only trouble with such a hypothesis is that it is difficult to prove. Gooch produces evidence that our own society, which he claims is derived from that of the Cro-Magnons, still shows traces of the social mores he ascribes to the Neanderthals. His theory is, essentially, that the Cro-Magnons, in wiping out the Neanderthals, accidentally incorporated the latter's 'dream' ideas into their culture – and that such ideas still survive today.

The hypothesis cannot be dismissed out of hand. Far, far more recently, at around the time when the Roman Empire was at its height, the Celts across Europe enjoyed a 'confederation' of which signs can still be seen today. A pure Scot arriving in New York, Cardiff or any other of the non-Scottish capitals can expect to be welcomed by other Celts, whatever their original nation and however many generations have passed since their ancestors left it.

The theory's great difficulty is, as noted, its considerable lack of proof. One reviewer, John Naughton in *The Observer*, went a little over the top when he remarked: 'How does Mr Gooch know all this? The answer is that he is guessing.' This is unfair criticism – Gooch produces a mass of indicative, albeit necessarily speculative, evidence in favour of his hypothesis – but nevertheless it is true that our knowledge of the past is and has to be based on the artefacts surviving from that past: lacking the artefacts, all we can do is make an educated deduction.

Whether or not we are prepared to accept that the Neanderthals had an advanced but abstract civilization, we are left with a question: what sort of civilization *did* the Neanderthals have? We do not know. We have evidence of cannibalism and other habits that we might consider a trifle unsavoury, but this does not mean that Neanderthal society was necessarily uncivilized. Killing people simply in order to satisfy hunger is hardly one of humanity's more endearing habits (and anyway seems always to have been rare), but the consumption of dead heroes can be seen as a mark of respect, in that the eaters may hope to inherit some of the admired qualities of the deceased. It is possible that wise Neanderthal men and women were only too delighted to allow themselves to be killed and eaten, on the basis that their souls would live on in newly inhabited bodies.

There are a few further questions:

- what sort of a civilization did the Cro-Magnons enjoy?
- did the Cro-Magnons indeed deliberately wipe out the Neanderthals?
- why were the Neanderthals, who as a species of human being had had a much longer pedigree, vulnerable to the Cro-Magnons?
- why, in any case, should the Cro-Magnons have felt the slightest urge to exterminate the Neanderthals (with whom it is thought they could have interbred)?

This last question is probably the most profound. In our own time it has been only fascists, racists and their ilk who have felt the urge to slaughter vast numbers of people whom they have regarded as 'different' from themselves. Thankfully it is comparatively rare for human beings to seek to exterminate those creatures whom they regard as very much their inferiors – it is hard to find someone who favours the meaningless slaughter of dogs, for example. But people are much more likely – and we should stress that only the lunatic fringe is involved – to believe it necessary that those they perceive as only *minimally* inferior to themselves should be annihilated. (The next stage, paradoxically, is to describe the 'inferiors' as animals, so that the slaughterers need have no qualms of conscience. This is how, for example, Hitler persuaded numerous Germans to murder Jews.)

Here we have a possible explanation of why the Cro-Magnons might have exterminated the Neanderthals: the Neanderthals were very like them, and therefore constituted a threat. The Neanderthals were, however, physically weaker, and so it was 'reasonable' to wipe them out, or at least to subjugate them to the extent that eventually they died out. (We see the same sort of philosophy working in countries like South Africa today.)

As to whether the Neanderthals had an advanced civilization, there is no possible answer to this question. Any traces have been obliterated by the advance of the ethos that we have inherited from our Cro-Magnon ancestors. We are now a technological species, and until comparatively recently we paid little attention to species that were not.

DID EXTRATERRESTRIALS VISIT THE EARTH IN THE DISTANT PAST?

There is a succinct and spiritually satisfying answer to this question: probably not.

There are several reasons for the response, of which two are significant. The first is that evidence for such a visit seems to be nonexistent. The second – much less scientific – is that the arguments put forward in popular potboilers supporting such a notion are in general so specious that one is embarrassed to allow oneself to be associated with them. It is largely for this latter, purely emotional reason that very few scientists will take the idea seriously. Those who do keep very quiet about it, although, as we have seen, the 'bootstraps' hypothesis concerning the origin of life is never totally dismissed by any but the most hidebound of life scientists.

The ancient-astronaut industry really got under way in 1969, with the first English-language publication of a book called *Chariots of the Gods?*, by Erich von Däniken. Von Däniken's first few lines – 'This was a very difficult book to write. It will be a very difficult book to read' – were true but less than prophetic, since people read it in their millions.

In fact, there were earlier ancient-astronaut theorists, including Desmond Leslie, who wrote with George Adamski the notorious *Flying Saucers Have Landed* (1953). Leslie tells us that aliens from Venus arrived on Earth in the year 18,617,841 BC. He knows this because he has been able to decipher 'ancient Brahmin tables'. This comes as something of a surprise, because the human species is only about four million years old, and the Brahmins substantially younger!

LEFT *George Adamski, the most famous of all claimed UFO abductees, peering through a Newtonian telescope . . . during the day!*

Another early theorist was W Raymond Drake, whose 1964 book *Gods or Spacemen* is heartily recommended to those in search of innocent mirth. He is, perhaps, in with a chance when he equates gods with the planets that bear their names: ancient legends of Jupiter doing nasty things to people could really represent an ancient memory that aliens from the *planet* Jupiter dropped nuclear bombs on Earth. All well and good until he extends his ideas to the god Uranus, which he enthusiastically does. Unfortunately, the planet Uranus was not discovered until 1781.

In a book published in 1974, *Mystery of the Ancients*, Craig and Eric Umland claimed that the aliens were still among us, in the form of the Maya. According to the Umlands, scientists in the USA and the USSR are currently competing to decipher the secrets of Mayan script in order to unlock the secrets of the Universe. Besides, the Maya knew of the wheel – and how could they have done so unless they had been told about it by extraterrestrial visitors?

All of these ideas are fun, of course, but they do not help us to answer the original question. If extraterrestrials visited humanity in the very early days of our species, the cultural impact must have been major – unless, that is, the extraterrestrials had the common sense not to interfere too much with whatever level of civilization then existed.

Very few studies have shown any evidence that extraterrestrials have ever visited the Earth. As always, however, there is an exception. Robert Temple, in his *The Sirius Mystery* (1976), examined reports of anthropologists concerning the Dogon tribe of North Africa. His analyses suggested that the Dogon knew that the planets of the Solar System went around the Sun in ellipses, rather than in circles; they knew

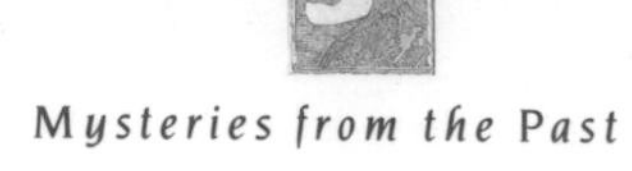

also that the dwarf-star companion of Sirius (the Pup) existed and was made up of very compressed matter. The Dogon were aware that the planet Saturn had rings and that the planet Jupiter had four moons, which are pieces of information that cannot be obtained without the use of a telescope – an artefact the Dogon have yet to discover.

Here we have a quandary. Jupiter has many more moons than four – we are still not certain of the number, and possibly never will be. The rings of Saturn are indeed spectacular, but we now know that Jupiter, Uranus and Neptune likewise have rings: it is strange that the visiting extraterrestrials should not have mentioned this.

The Dogon were almost certainly visited late in the nineteenth century by missionaries who were up-to-date in terms of modern science. The small, hot and compact companion of Sirius was discovered in 1915 – the first real investigation of the Dogon did not take place until at least the 1930s and 1940s. But it seems far from unlikely that other explorers might have visited the Dogon in the intervening period, passing on the latest scientific information.

There is another aspect to the ancient-astronaut hypothesis: perhaps our remote ancestors could not have survived had it not been for the fact that they were *destined* to do so. But such ideas are heresy . . .

Has the Earth Flipped Over at Least Once in the Past?

In 1982 Peter Warlow published a book called *The Reversing Earth*. It is generally recognized that the magnetic field of the Earth has periodically reversed: Warlow claimed that the Earth as a whole had flipped over. In so doing he was supporting the ideas of Immanuel Velikovsky (1895–1979), one of the earliest of the modern breed of pseudoscientists.

Velikovskianism seems set to make a sudden resurgence after all these years. The neo-Velikovskians are, refreshingly, starting to apply some of the tools of science in their arguments: such knotty subjects as physics and mathematics are beginning to make their appearance. Unfortunately, they are doing so alongside all the inherited pseudoscience and woolly thinking, the pretentious massing of obscure and unreliable (and unreliably dated) data which have traditionally marked Velokovskianism off from more orthodox science.

Velikovsky's ideas are wide-ranging, but we can sum them up by saying that, about 3500 years ago, the planet Venus was born as a comet, spat from a volcano on the planet Jupiter. This comet lurched around the Solar System before settling into its current orbital position. Most notably, it had several close encounters with the Earth, causing great upheavals, dividing the Red Sea, spattering the landscape with flaming petroleum, and in general making life sheer hell for our ancestors. One of its major effects on our planet was to cause it to flip 'upside-down' on its axis.

Velikovsky's *Worlds in Collision* produced an overreaction from the scientific establishment for the simple reason that Velikovsky had cast his net far and wide in search of supporting evidence for his theory. Since no scientist was prepared to sit down and do a comparable amount of research in order to demolish a theory which seemed so patently to be a load of rubbish, they all simply cried 'Rubbish!' and stamped their feet. Astronomers noted that the archaeology was interesting and archaeologists said that the astronomy seemed to make a lot of sense.

The overall effect has been unfortunate in two different ways. First, the Velikovskians have been given the chance to make a superficially plausible claim that there is some kind of 'orthodox-science' vendetta against them and against their 'master': they have been able to portray themselves as persecuted martyrs. Second, the furore obscured the fact that Velikovsky was making an important point: catastrophes *have* occurred in the past. Until recent years this idea was largely pooh-poohed by the scientific community. A second point Velikovsky made was that evidence of such catastrophes could be deduced from ancient writings, oral legends and the like.

There were, of course, flaws in Velikovsky's reasoning: his imagined catastrophes were fanciful and, while it is all very well to derive clues from oral legends, it makes little sense to prefer these to properly researched results.

In *The Reversing Earth* Warlow tried to prove that, during the last 13,000 or so years, the Earth has flipped over on its axis about five times. He employed the conventional Velikovskian technique of selecting evidence while at the same time adopting much of the traditional (that is, false) Velikovskian lore. It is worth going through his arguments in some detail, because they represent the very best of the theories concerning the idea that the Earth has periodically flipped on its axis.

FAR LEFT *The Earth from space, as photographed in 1972 by Apollo 17.* **ABOVE** *Photograph of the giant planet Jupiter taken in 1979 by Voyager 1, showing two of the planet's moons, Io and Europa. The Great Red Spot is clearly visible.*

In the ordinary way, turning over a massive spinning object like a planet is a difficult task. Anyone who has ever played with a gyroscope will know that the object displays a distinct aversion to being turned upside-down; in many ways the spinning Earth can be viewed as a sort of super-heavy gyroscope. Warlow pointed out, quite correctly, that this is not the sort of inversion we should be looking at: if the Earth flipped over in this way the Sun would still rise in the east, whereas there are legends that, before the (undescribed) catastrophe, the Sun rose in the west, and that it is only since that catastrophe that the Sun has risen in the east.

There is, however, a different way in which spinning objects can turn over. This is exemplified by a children's toy called the tippe-top. Most tippe-tops come from Christmas crackers; they look like an apple with a fat stem. The tippe-top has two delights. First, if you spin it on the table, 'stalk'-upward, it almost immediately flips itself over to spin upside-down, balancing on the stalk'. The second and more exciting aspect is that, when it does so, the direction of spin is not affected: if the initial spin was clockwise, it will still be clockwise even after the toy has turned over. This is exactly the opposite of what common sense might predict. We can note, too, that the tippe-top differs markedly from the gyroscope: a tippe-top turns over spontaneously – indeed, it is hard to stop it from doing so – whereas a considerable amount of effort is required to flip over a gyroscope.

This, then, would appear to be an easy way to turn the Earth over – and one in better accord with the legends than the (probably impossible) straightforward one. However, problems arise as soon as you start to think about what is actually happening when a tippe-top flips over. The mathematics – and indeed the physics – of the situation are extremely complicated, but we can note that the tippe-top is not operating in isolation. The complete system involved includes a flat surface – a table, perhaps – and a steady downward gravitational pull. Unfortunately, there aren't any tables in space.

What, even so, of the required gravitational pull? To answer this question we are led back to the idea of big gassy planets like Jupiter spitting out small rocky ones like Venus, which then play a sort of cosmic billiards before settling down. Warlow and his supporters point to the fact that certain quasars (highly energetic galaxies) have jets of material emerging from their cores: could it not be that stars and big gassy planets can behave analogously? This is only superficially a valid question, since quasars are in every respect very different objects from stars and planets. Also, the jets of material associated with them seem certainly to shoot out from the rotational poles and to keep travelling that way; were new planets to engage in the game of cosmic billiards they would have to shoot out equatorially from their 'parents'.

There are further problems with the whole scenario. Jupiter is a very massive planet, and its escape velocity is correspondingly high. Venus is much smaller, but nevertheless still has about the same mass as the Earth. To accelerate a body with the mass of Venus to the escape velocity of Jupiter would require a fairly impressive 'spit'!

Then again, for a planet with Venus's mass to have a gravitational effect on the Earth even as strong as that of the Moon, it would have to pass within about four million kilometres (2,500,000 miles). This distance may seem large, but it is dwarfed by the length of the Earth's orbit – 9,300,000,000km (5,800,000,000 miles). In other words, the chances of Venus having even this negligible effect on the Earth are only about 1 in 115 per transit of our planet's orbit. And this is assuming that Venus is travelling in exactly the same plane as the Earth's orbit, which it probably wouldn't be. If we allow Venus five transits of the orbit, the chances of its affecting the Earth are still only about 28:1 against.

Warlow's claim that the Earth has flipped five times over 13,000 years implies a cosmic near miss every 2600 years. So where are all the planets? Even laundering the figures in Warlow's favour, only one out of every 28 newborn planets will have any effect on us, so planets must be popping out from somewhere every century or so. There must be tens of millions of them out there!

One can go on in this knockabout vein for some time, because some of the illogicalities of the Velikovskian scientists are very funny indeed. However, this does not mean that they are necessarily wrong in their idea that the Earth may have flipped over, simply that they haven't adequately worked out what could cause it to do so. And we have to acknowledge that, although it is difficult to flip planets over, there is good evidence that similar things have happened in the past among the outer planets of the Solar System. For example, Uranus, which is much more massive than the Earth, seems to have been tipped over so that it lies on its side. Triton, the largest satellite of Neptune, goes round the

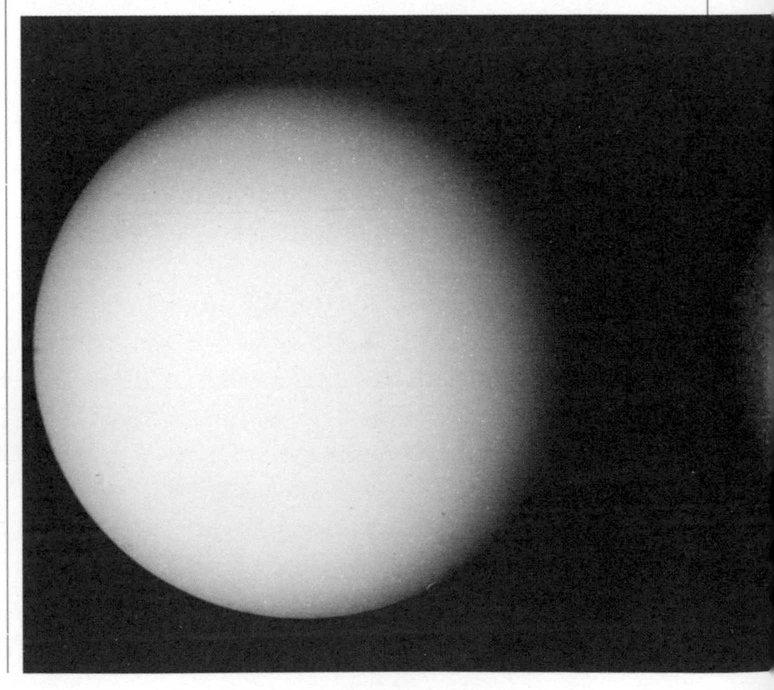

planet in the opposite direction to Neptune's other moons, and may originally have been a small planet in its own right which was captured by Neptune's gravity. The little double planet Pluto has such a weird orbit that, even though almost all of the time it is by a long way the furthest known planet from the Sun, occasionally (as at the time of writing) it is closer to the Sun than is Neptune. One explanation for this is that the two bodies constituting Pluto were originally moons of Neptune, but that something tore them from the giant planet's grasp – the converse of what is thought to have happened to Triton! Clearly some very large forces have disrupted the outer regions of the Solar System at some stage, or stages, in the past, but we have no idea of when or of what they might have been.

So it is not an impossibility that the Earth has indeed been flipped over, or at least tilted, during remote or even not so remote prehistory.

Before leaving this particular mystery, we should repeat that there is good proof that the direction of the Earth's magnetic field has indeed flipped many times during our planet's lifetime. (The reasons are fairly well understood, but need not concern us here.) Interestingly, the next flip is rather overdue, so do not be surprised to wake up tomorrow and find that your compass isn't working properly!

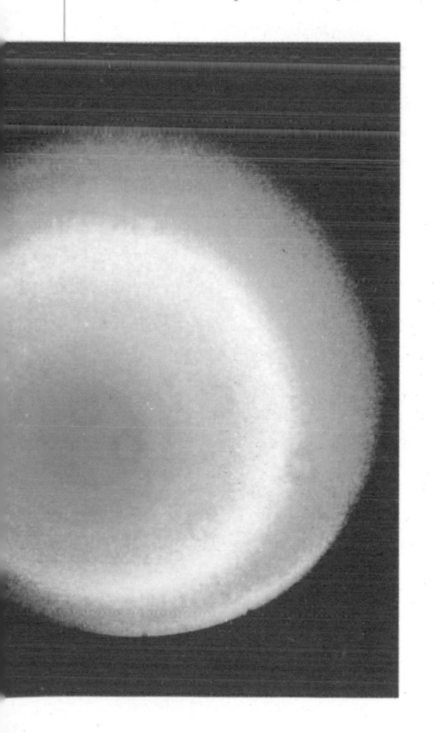

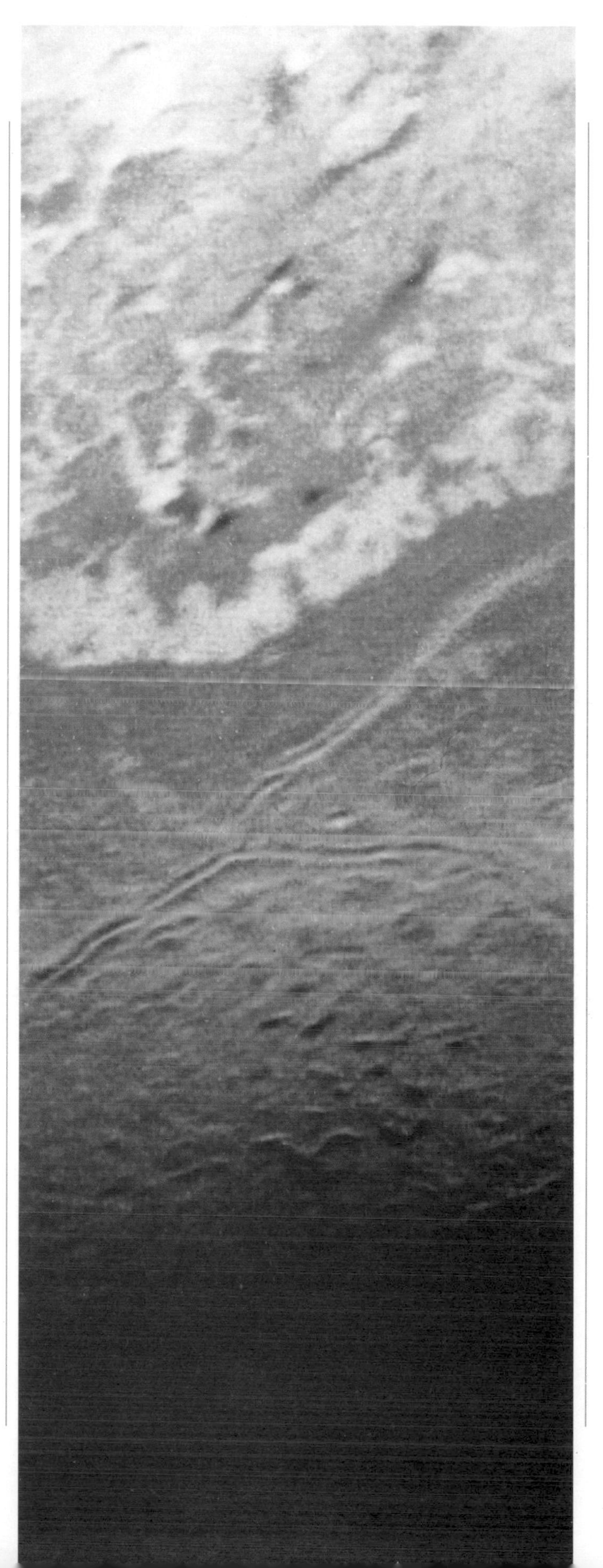

LEFT *Images of Uranus built up from information sent back in 1986 by Voyager 2; the image on the right is in false colour and extreme contrast enhancement to show details of Uranus's polar regions.* **RIGHT** *A Voyager 2 image from 1989 of part of the surface of Triton, Neptune's large moon.*

Why Do Ice Ages Happen?

One of the most infuriating habits of the scientifically illiterate is to talk of the 'ice age' as if there had been only one. In fact, there have been several ice ages, possibly many. Furthermore, it seems likely that the 'most recent' ice age is in fact still continuing: we are probably enjoying one of the interglacials, or warmer periods, of this ice age.

There is a certain amount of debate as to why ice ages occur. They seem to have happened periodically over the last 900 million years, and may have been doing so since the early days of Earth (the longer ago something happened, the less likely it is that we will have tripped over the evidence). The ice ages we know about are dated as follows:

- 2300 million years ago (probably two or three ice ages, but the dating here is vague)
- 900 million years ago
- 750 million years ago
- 600 million years ago
- 450 million years ago
- 300 million years ago
- current

Intriguingly, there is very little evidence of any widespread glaciation 150 million years ago, during the geological period known as the Jurassic. This lacuna may be of interest in trying to establish the circumstances, or complex of circumstances, required if an ice age is to occur . . . assuming, of course, that the neat spacing of the others is not just a matter of chance.

A good correlation can be seen between the occurrence of an ice age and various other geographical/geological phenomena:

- there is a substantial landmass near one of the poles – in the case of the current ice age, Antarctica fits the bill
- extensive mountain-building, due to colliding continental plates, is in progress – the Andes, Himalayas and Cascades are all mountain ranges that have come into existence during the past 10+ million years, and are still in the process of creation
- more landmasses are above water than usual – although this may be a chicken-and-egg effect because during an ice age much of the world's water is locked up as ice, so that ocean levels are lower

None of these circumstances pertained during the Jurassic, but this does not mean that mountain-building and the proximity of a large landmass to one or other of the poles, taken together, constitute the cause of an ice age. After all, the coincidence could not be expected to occur so neatly every 150 million years.

It is not hard to see how these two phenomena might, as it were, assist an ice age on its way. A continental landmass located at the north or south pole is likely to be ice-covered, and therefore very reflective: a lot of the impinging sunlight will be reflected back out into space. Similarly, high

LEFT *Glaciation in Greenland underscores the fact that the Earth is currently undergoing one of its periodic ice ages. We are lucky enough to be living during a warm period (interglacial) of this ice age, but our luck cannot last forever; at some time during the next few thousand, few hundred or even just few years the next cold period (glacial) will commence unless humanity's pollution contributes so much to the greenhouse effect that global warming prevents the glaciers from spreading. The future of our species seems to be gloomy, either way. However, humanity could survice a glacial; its chances of surviving a runaway greenhouse effect are much more slender.*

RIGHT *The Pleiades cluster. The ancient Greeks identified and named the seven brightest stars; today we can see only six with the naked eye. In fact the cluster contains countless young stars.*

mountains (and mountains are highest when new, before erosion wears them down) will be covered in snow and ice, and once again will reflect sunlight. The net effect is that the total amount of energy from the Sun available to the Earth is reduced a little, so that the globe as a whole becomes slightly cooler. This minor cooling, in itself, is unlikely to be sufficient to precipitate an ice age but, where other circumstances are favourable, may be just enough to tip the balance.

So we must look around for phenomena that occur every 150 million years or so. One suggestion has been that the energy output of the Sun itself fluctuates over a long period. This is a reasonable hypothesis. We know of other stars whose brightness changes periodically, over a timespan of hours, weeks or years. That stars can vary over much longer periods seems likely. To take a single indicative example that this might be so we can turn our attention to a star cluster named by the ancient Greeks the Pleiades, or Seven Sisters. One sister, Merope, was represented by a fainter star than the rest because, according to the myth, she took as mate a mortal, Sisyphus, rather than a god, like the others. The interesting point is that the Greeks were certainly able to see Merope with the naked eye, whereas today this is virtually impossible. Of course, it is feasible that the Greeks were more sharp-sighted than we are, and certainly their skies were clearer; but it is equally likely that Merope has dimmed a fair deal over the past few thousand years – in other words, that it is a variable star with a period of at least several thousand years. From here we can suggest that, perhaps, *all* stars vary their output periodically, but that for obvious practical reason we have no way of knowing that this is so in the case of stars whose periods are sufficiently long. (Who could set up a series of astronomical observations lasting one million years, let alone 150 million?)

The putative variability of the Sun's output is an intriguing idea; the hypothesis is to a slight extent supported by 'the mystery of the missing neutrinos'. The fact that the Sun is producing far less of these enigmatic particles than expected could well be a symptom that it is going through a quiescent period – although it could equally well be that there is something wrong with our theories concerning what makes the Sun shine.

A different suggestion is that the rate of the Earth's spin periodically slows down and then speeds up again, the 'slow' times coinciding with ice ages. However, it is not immediately obvious why this should be, and it is difficult to conjecture a mechanism whereby, once slowed, the spin could then be speeded up again.

Another factor that must be taken into account is that our Sun is not motionless in space; instead, it travels around the centre of the Galaxy once every 220 million years or so. In the process, it regularly encounters regions where space contains a more than usual amount of matter in the form of gas, dust and other debris. This has various effects. For example, the amount of the Sun's light reaching the Earth is reduced at such times, although it is hard to guess whether or not this would be significant. Perhaps more important, the Earth would be subjected to a greater than usual bombardment of material from space. This would make little difference except on the occasions when, by ill luck, one or more such items of infalling material happened to be big. As we have seen, the impact of a very large meteorite or cometary nucleus caused sufficient damage to our global climate that the dinosaurs and much of the rest of the existing lifeforms were extinguished. Experiencing several such impacts in a comparatively short period of time might well be sufficient to trigger an ice age – assuming the other circumstances noted above were suitable.

However, as will be evident, we are really still guessing as to the true cause of ice ages. One point favouring all theories that rely on changes affecting the Solar System as a whole, rather than changes confined merely to the Earth, is that the planet Mars is currently, like our own world, in the throes of an ice age. Various surface features on that world seem to show for certain that the planet has, in the past, enjoyed running water, but today there is none to be seen. In all likelihood, the water is frozen under the ground (there is also a fair amount in the planet's ice-caps). That both planets should be suffering ice ages simultaneously may, of course, be just a matter of coincidence; but it seems more likely that there is a common cause.

Will Linear A Ever Be Deciphered?

The forms of written languages undergo constant evolution – as an example, we need only compare a piece of medieval script with a modern printed newspaper. During its 1100 years of ascendance, from about 2500BC to 1400BC, the Minoan civilization of Crete used two forms of script. First, as with many civilizations, came hieroglyphics. Then, around 1700BC, the Minoans developed from the hieroglyphic script a new syllabic form, today called Linear A. When the Mycenaeans invaded Crete they adapted Linear A to produce a revised form, Linear B. Both scripts have been preserved on clay tablets, most of which are inventories; however, only a few hundred examples of Linear A exist, whereas there are some thousands of surviving tablets bearing Linear B.

Deciphering the scripts of the ancients is not an easy business, especially if those scripts do not form part of the 'family tree' of any currently existing script. For example, the meanings of ancient Egyptian hieroglyphs were unknown until, by chance, a 'dictionary' came to light. This was the famous Rosetta Stone, discovered in 1799. On it was inscribed the same text in three different scripts – Egyptian hieroglyphic and demotic as well as, most importantly, Greek. The British polymath Thomas Young (1773–1829), using the fact

LEFT *The Rosetta Stone.*
ABOVE *A statuette of the Minoan Snake Goddess discovered at Knossos.*
RIGHT *The queen's apartments at Knossos.*

that the name of Ptolemy appeared several times, was able to decipher part of the hieroglyphics. After Young's death his work was carried on by the French Egyptologist Jean-François Champollion (1790–1832). However, without the lucky discovery of the Rosetta Stone, it is likely that Egyptian hieroglyphics would still be a mystery to us.

No such 'dictionary' exists in the case of Linear A and Linear B. However, a brilliant young British scholar, Michael Ventris (1922–56), recognized in 1952 that Linear B was the written version of a language akin to Greek, and thanks to this inspiration made swift progress in deciphering it. Tragically, he died in a road accident just four years after starting. His work on Linear B was carried on with flair by John Chadwick (b. 1920). Ventris died before he had had the time to turn his attentions to Linear A, about which he is reported to have had some initial ideas.

Our inability to penetrate Linear A is something of a mystery. After all, as we've noted, Linear B is a development from the earlier script, and so the decipherment of one should provide a very useful clue to the other. Perhaps we shall be lucky and discover another 'dictionary' like the Rosetta Stone.

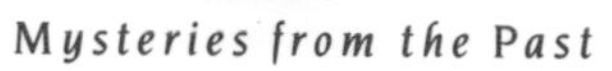

Why Did The Ancients Build Megalithic Monuments?

The use of very large stones – megaliths – either singly or in combination was widespread among the ancients, and it is clear that our ancestors must have regarded the practice as extremely important. After all, the transportation of such huge and heavy slabs of rock, often over long distances, must have required an incredible investment of effort on the part of any society possessing only rudimentary technology. The subsequent erection of the monuments – for example, capping the uprights of Stonehenge – likewise cannot have been easy. Indeed, some people have suggested that it was so difficult as to have been impossible, but this is to underestimate the intelligence and ingenuity of our forebears. Modern engineers have demonstrated, at least on paper, construction techniques that would certainly have been possible using the equipment available to Neolithic and later cultures. Which is far from saying that the task was *easy*.

That these monuments were vitally important to our ancestors is, therefore, obvious. However, the motives for

LEFT *The Sphinx with, behind it, the pyramid of Khafra, son of Cheops.* ABOVE *Some of the stones at Carnac, Brittany (France).*

building them are, in most cases, very much less so. We can understand why the Egyptian culture built the Pyramids: self-aggrandisement on the part of the pharaohs. After the first of them, the Step Pyramid, had been built (probably by Imhotep) for the pharaoh Zoser in the third millennium BC, all the other pharaohs wanted one too. Since the pharaohs were gods on Earth, the luckless culture had little choice but to kowtow to their whims, and vast amounts of expense and slave-power were devoted to the construction of these monuments. The rather dissimilar, and much later, pyramids of South America were probably largely religious in origin; if one wants to build a pretty impressive temple to one's gods, the pyramid is as good a shape as any to choose.

Elsewhere, in places as diverse as Western Europe and Easter Island, the motives are little understood – and still hotly debated. For a long time it was assumed by archaeologists that here, too, the purpose was religious. However, this was before the astronomers, notably Professor Alexander Thom, got in on the act. Thom examined countless stone circles and other megalithic monuments with an almost monomaniacal zeal, paying particular attention to the alignments of various of their features with events of astronomical importance – for example, the position on the horizon of the rising Sun at the winter solstice. It was perhaps not surprising that he found such alignments: the dating of events such as the solstices and equinoxes is very important to an agricultural society dependent on the cycle of the seasons. The importance is certainly practical; by extension it is likely to become religious as well.

But Thom did not stop there. He began to seek further alignments which might relate to far more subtle astronomical changes – and found them. For example, there was the matter of lunar *standstills*. Because of the way that the Moon moves in its orbit around the Earth, its place of rising on the horizon varies a little, each night moving a tiny amount further north until its position of rising seems to come to a halt (a standstill) before moving back southwards again. The whole cycle, from north to south to north, takes 18.61 years. However, things are not that simple. Because the period is

RIGHT *Stonehenge, England: sunrise at the midsummer solstice.*

not a whole number of years, the next standstill will occur at a different season than its predecessor. Here lies the rub. If the standstill occurs in midwinter, the rising point will be at its most northerly; if in midsummer, the point is at its *most southerly* – and the picture is even further complicated during the intermediate times of year! The effect is, therefore, an infernally hard one to spot ... and yet Thom found more alignments with standstills than could realistically be explained by chance.

Many archaeologists were unable to swallow Thom's arguments – some because they were ignorant of astronomy and others, perhaps more reasonably, because the notion that our 'primitive' forebears could have such an advanced observational astronomy was anathema to them. When, around 1963, Gerald Hawkins applied a computer to the various alignments of features present at Stonehenge, finding their astronomical connotations, the storm burst. Thom could safely be publicly discounted as an eccentric (he was indeed something of an eccentric in many of his personal habits) and a generally irrelevant gadfly, but it was rather more difficult to depict Hawkins's computer in the same light. Entrenched archaeologists, desperate to refute the 'heresy' by any means, came out with some astonishing counter-arguments. Perhaps the most ludicrous was this:

- Hawkins required a computer to 'decode' Stonehenge, showing its function as an astronomical observatory
- our forebears did not have computers
- therefore, how could they have constructed Stonehenge as an astronomical observatory?

Bumble-bees do not have advanced knowledge of aeronautical science, yet some extremely complicated maths is required to explain why it is that a bumble-bee can fly. Does this mean that bumble-bees cannot fly? Obviously not. Yet this was the sort of argument used by various archaeologists, notably Glyn Daniel, who refused to accept the findings of Thom, Hawkins and a growing number of others.

In more recent years the controversy has died down a little, although it has still not ceased. It seems probable that, to our ancestors, there was no clear boundary between fields of endeavour that we now consider to be quite separate – for example, astronomy and religion. The significance of the

Sun's activities was extreme, because they affected the food-supply. It is a small jump from this to the veneration of the Sun as an important god. The behaviour of the Sun was therefore well worth watching, because it could influence the coming harvest. It would therefore seem to make a lot of sense to construct edifices that would allow you to observe the Sun's behaviour because, as a god, he might angrily starve you or beneficently reward you with plenty. The megalithic monuments can therefore be regarded in part as religious structures, in part as astronomical observatories, and in part as clocks, allowing our ancestors to record precisely the various cyclical changes of the celestial bodies.

These are speculations: to call them any more than that would be foolhardy. Nevertheless, we can conclude that many of the megalithic monuments had some sort of astronomical import (and this includes some aspects of the Egyptian Pyramids); as to their religious meaning we can only guess. A further mystery is this: if we assume that the motive for building the monuments was a mixture of religion and astronomy, which way round did the process operate? In other words, did the religious belief stimulate the precise astronomical observation, or was it that the study of the skies gave rise to beliefs about the gods?

This question is impossible to answer. If we look at, for example, Graeco-Roman mythology, we discover that the constellations in the night sky can be directly equated with gods, goddesses, heroes and other mythological notables. Did the ancients watch the heavens and, from what they saw there, construct their whole complicated pantheon? Or was it that they developed their legends of the deities and then 'saw' those deities portrayed in the sky? Why did the ancients identify the planets with such important deities – Mars, Venus, Jupiter and the rest? For that matter, why was the Moon – by far the most obvious object in the night sky – equated with only a minor deity, Diana? Would the whole story not have made more sense had Jupiter been identified with the Sun, Venus with the Moon, and so on?

The reasons for this apparent perversity are probably now lost to us for all time. However, who knows, perhaps someday we'll come across some tablet or document that will make the whole thing clear. Until then all we can do is wait . . . and wonder.

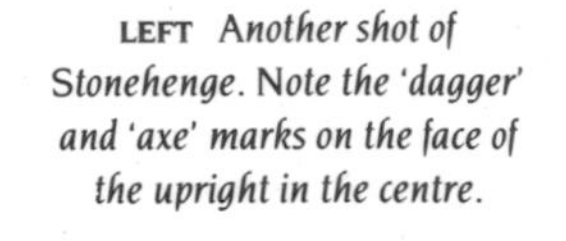

LEFT *Another shot of Stonehenge. Note the 'dagger' and 'axe' marks on the face of the upright in the centre.*

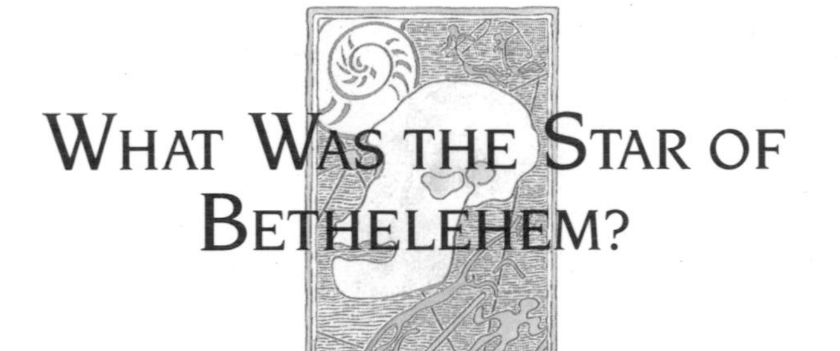

What Was the Star of Bethelehem?

Not so many years ago, this would have been a non-question: Christians believed that the Star was one of God's miracles, while scientists, by and large, believed that the whole story was a myth. More recently, these hidebound attitudes have changed, in that educated, intelligent Christians accept that there is little need for God to perform a miracle (unless, moving in mysterious ways, He particularly wants to) when He can create the same effect using natural processes; while scientists have begun more and more to recognize that there may be more truth in the mystical writings of the Christian and other religions than they have previously been prepared to admit. This latter point is not intended to imply that scientists have suddenly 'got God'; rather that they have generally refused to admit that, if some event is widely reported in religious writings, there is a very good chance that it did in fact happen.

Leaving aside the straightforwardly miraculous, there are two major possible explanations for the Star of Bethlehem. One is that a comparatively nearby star in our Galaxy exploded as a supernova, shining millions of times more brightly than usual. A second is that a rare conjunction of certain bright planets created the image of a very bright star. (A third possible explanation is that the whole story was made up, to impress unbelievers, by the apostle Matthew or whoever wrote the gospel ascribed to him. This hypothesis does not seem to have a lot going for it because, at the time Matthew – or whoever – was writing, there would still have been a few people around who could say something like 'I don't remember any star!')

The idea that the Star might have been a supernova was touchingly treated in a 1955 story by the science-fiction writer Arthur C Clarke, 'The Star'. He was not, so far as we can tell, putting forward the idea as a serious theory: his purpose was to tell a good story. Nevertheless, the idea is extremely plausible. We can look at it from both agnostic and religious viewpoints. The appearance in the skies of a bright 'new' star would certainly have influenced the ideas of our astrology-prone ancestors: this was a sign of major import. The coincidence of the Star's appearance with the birth of a self-proclaimed Messiah such as Christ would, certainly, have increased his 'street cred': as one of a succession of putative Messiahs and/or revolutionary leaders (all, so far, failed), he could claim that his birth had been heralded by this unusual celestial event. If we decide to be less cynical, we could suggest that God triggered a supernova at exactly the right time to draw the Magi towards the place where His son was being born.

It is difficult to establish which of the two scientific theories could hold sway. In recent years the idea that the Star was a supernova has been propounded by, among others, AT Lawton, a past President of the British Interplanetary Society. He notes that, although nearby supernovae are somewhat rare, an event such as this occurring in 4BC would make a lot of statistical sense. Of course, he has very little proof (how could he have?), but his various arguments are very persuasive.

Equally so are those of David Hughes, another distinguished astronomer and the author of *The Star of Bethlehem Mystery* (1979). Hughes points to a conjunction (appearance in the same point of the sky) of the two major planets Jupiter and Saturn in 7BC, a reasonable year for Christ's birth. The brilliance of this conjunction would certainly have been important to ancient astrologers: the three Magi, on the reasonable assumption that they were students of the skies, might very likely have followed the 'star' to its 'source'.

The ideas of Hughes are immediately provable: there was indeed a conjunction of the two great planets in the year he identifies. But there is a problem: the astrologers of the ancient world were certainly *au fait* with the behaviour of the planets and so, while they might have been excited by the conjunction of Jupiter and Saturn, they would not necessarily have regarded it as too desperately important. A supernova, by contrast, would have been a 'one-off' phenomenon – and hence much more likely to be the herald of the arrival of someone of importance.

Discovering the remnants of the supernovae of the past is a chancy business. When we are lucky, the orientation of spin of the resulting pulsars is such that we can place and date the initial explosion with some accuracy. Most of the time, though, we are unlucky: the supernova remnant is invisible to us, although we may be fortunate enough to observe the expanding cloud of gases and other matter receding from the pulsar. So far, no one has found a possible candidate for the supernova that might have represented the Star of Bethlehem.

LEFT *Detail of a 16th-century woodcut, possibly by* Holbein, *showing an astronomer observing a celestial body.* Early *astronomers did not have telescopes to assist their observations, but nevertheless they had a full knowledge of the skies.* **RIGHT** A *Portuguese sunset. One little discussed possibility is that the Star of Bethlehem was in fact simply the setting Sun, which the Magi followed westwards.*

Kr
A
Hg

PART TWO

Mysteries Of Life

Life itself is something of a mystery. Most chemists will tell you that, once chemical reactions become complex enough, the end result will be life. But this explanation is not sufficient to explain the phenomenon: there is a definite difference between, shall we say, an amoeba and a crystal, yet the crystal grows and (in a very limited sense) reproduces – two activities that are generally assumed to be characteristic of living material.

So what is it that differentiates life from the nonliving? The distinction is not clear: at the same time that we recognize it, we cannot define it. We have similar difficulties when we look at such aspects as soul and intelligence: these have a profound effect on our daily existence, yet we have problems whenever we try to quantify them. After all, what is intelligence? It seems to us to be an evolutionary survival factor: the more intelligent a species, the more likely it is to survive in the long term; this is a reasonable hypothesis, but it can hardly be considered as any more than that.

When we look at the mysteries of life we must look also at phenomena that seem, on the face of it, to have little to do with the way that life works.

LEFT *Artificially grown crystals of one of the alums (aluminium ammonium sulphate).* **BELOW** *The great 19th-century scientist Friedrich Wöhler who prepared the first organic compound derived from inorganic chemicals. This was the death-knell for theories that organic chemicals possessed some 'vital force' unavailable to the inorganic chemicals.*

Do Human Beings Have a Soul?

Aristotle, who lived during the 4th century BC, said that there was a fundamental 'living principle' – or 'life force' – that distinguished living from nonliving material. The gods breathed 'vitalism' into living creatures, thereby giving them the quality of life. This life-principle was very important to the early alchemists: they saw it as so real that, not only did they consider all entities to be made up of differing proportions of dead matter and life force (spirit), they tried to use the spirit as, in essence, just one more chemical. As far as the alchemists were concerned the spirit of human beings and other living creatures was a quantifiable characteristic. Living creatures had 'vitalism': this was the distinction between them and the nonliving. Even the important German chemist Georg Ernst Stahl (1660–1734) supported these ideas.

In 1828 the theory started to fall to pieces. In that year the German chemist Friedrich Wöhler (1800–92) found a way of producing from inorganic materials the chemical urea; always beforehand this had been assumed to be a substance that could be produced only by bodily (biochemical) reactions. Later, in the 1840s, Emil Du Bois-Reymond (1818–96) showed experimentally that the impulses travelling along nerves are rather like the flow of electrical currents along a wire (the similarity is in fact even closer than he imagined). Later, in 1894, Max Rubner (1854–1932) demonstrated that the quantity of energy extracted from food by the body is largely determined by the laws of thermodynamics. The 1896 discovery by Eduard Buchner (1860–1917) that fermentation could carry on in the absence of living cells seemed like the final nail in the coffin.

But the lid of the coffin refuses to stay nailed down. One very important reason concerns Kirlian photography. Such photographs (named for Semyon and Valentina Kirlian, who explored the technique) seem to show auras – glowing

RIGHT *Georg Ernst Stahl, a chief promoter of the phlogiston theory; he was also a supporter of vitalism and an exceptionally sloppy scientist.*

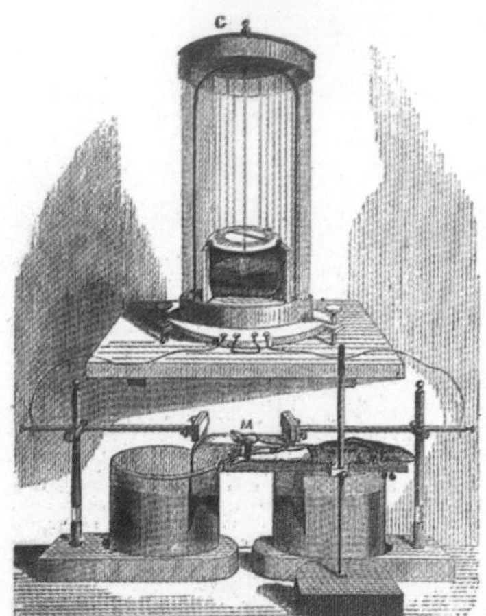

ABOVE *Emil Du Bois-Reymond, the 19th-century German physiologist who showed that muscular nerve impulses were akin to electricity.* **LEFT** *His equipment set up to demonstrate this fact using an unfortunate frog.* **BOTTOM** *Du Bois-Reymond demonstrating his apparatus for investigating muscular current and electric potential.*

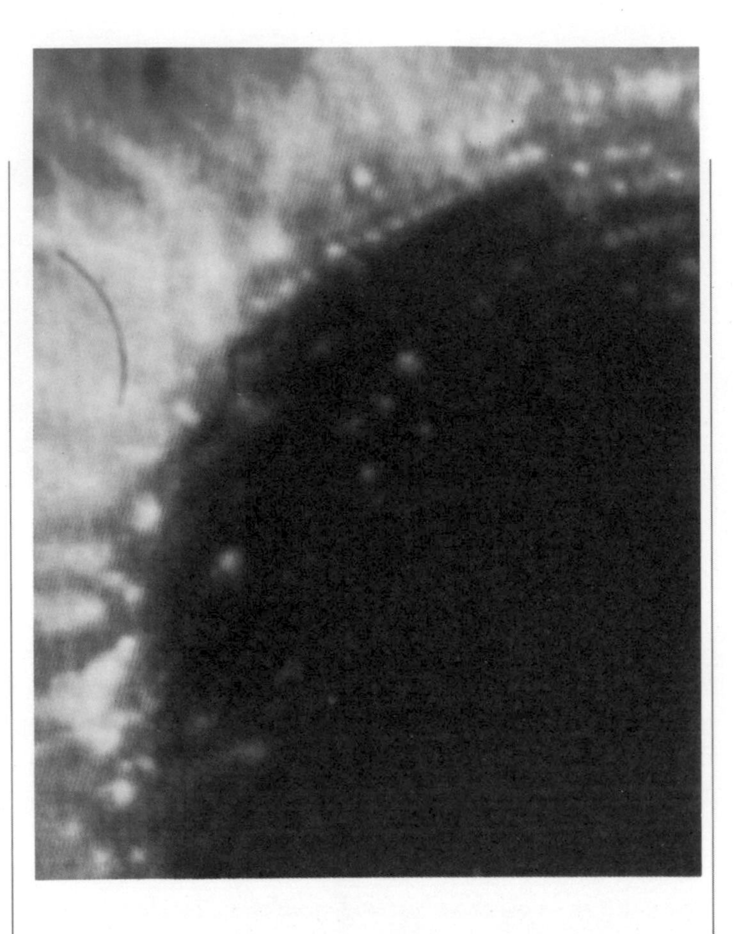

ABOVE *Part of a Kirlian photograph of the fingertip of a drug addict. There could hardly be a stronger contrast between this and the picture* **RIGHT** *which shows a Kirlian photograph of a healthy person's fingertip.*

haloes – around the margins of living and even recently dead organisms. Could these be photographs of the vitalistic ('soul') field of living creatures? Might it not be that the glowing auras are in fact photographs of the soul?

We have to reserve judgement. It seems not unlikely that human beings – and other living organisms – are surrounded by electromagnetic fields that could be picked up by cameras, assuming the circumstances were favourable. To leap from this standpoint to the assumption that we have an everlasting soul is to leap a very long way – probably too far.

Nevertheless, we can perceive that there is a difference between living (or recently dead) and nonliving material, and the Kirlian field is in some way involved with this. Such a differentiation could be as fundamental as life's ability to reproduce. Of course, to use such an argument to support vitalism would be specious: it is a nonsense to believe that only the presence of a 'vital principle' can confer life.

As for the soul? All we can do is guess.

Are There Other Intelligences?

Human beings have, traditionally, had a very high opinion of themselves. For millennia it was accepted that the Earth was at the centre of the Universe, despite all the contrary evidence, on the grounds that no other site would be fitting for the world on which the 'chosen' (whatever their religion) dwelt. Even today, fundamentalists envisage a Heaven barred to animals because, after all, only human beings were created in God's image and have souls. The idea that there might be intelligent lifeforms – indeed, civilizations more advanced than our own – on other worlds has been resisted vociferously by fundamentalists of various religions and, astonishingly, by a few scientists. The fact that even on our own planet we have creatures – the dolphins and whales – whose intelligence is at the very least comparable with our own makes little impact on people who deny the possible existence of intelligent life on other worlds.

One assumption is that any intelligent species will in due course develop a technology, just as we have done. This assumption is not borne out by any evidence – after all, the dolphins have no perceivable technology – but it is fair to guess that at least *some* intelligent species will develop an advanced technology. Those who rebut any ideas of extraterrestrial civilizations ask what seems at first sight to be a very salient question: 'Where *are* they all?' If the Universe is teeming with technological civilizations, why have they not come to visit us? At the very least, why have we not picked up traces of their domestic radio and television?

Why not, indeed? Yet, at the same time, why do we assume that a technological civilization will have the slightest desire to quest among the stars? We generally think that our own civilization does, but this belief is barely matched by governmental investment in the overall effort. Anyway, interstellar travel would be amazingly expensive – perhaps too expensive for most civilizations to contemplate. And why should we expect to have detected leakages from the domestic radio and television transmissions of our hypothetical aliens when we have made no effort to do so? If programmes aiming to pick up directly beamed 'contact' messages from other worlds are starved of funding, what possibility is there of anyone picking up the incredibly faint traces of extraterrestrial radio leakage? A further point concerns time. Despite the fact that our genus has been around for some four million years, it is only in the past century or so that we have discovered the knack of using radio signals. It is surely rather a lot to ask an alien species, perhaps 50 light-years away, to pick up the faintest of traces and then instantly respond. Even if the species did so, we would have little or no chance of picking up the message, because – to repeat – we are not looking out for it.

All discussions of extraterrestrial civilizations therefore have to be purely speculative. Some of the speculations have been extremely silly – and this is not to talk solely of the outpourings of the more sensationalist flying-saucer fans and their 'little green men'. For example, at a National Academy of Sciences meeting in Green Bank, West Virginia, in 1961, the otherwise distinguished US radio astronomer Frank Drake produced an impressive mathematical formula which purported to allow us to calculate roughly how many civilizations in our Galaxy would have developed a technology sufficient to allow them to make radio communication with us. When the equation is worked through, we discover that there should be at most 50,000 and at least 40 such civilizations. This is very impressive, until we start looking at some of the factors in the equation:

- ► the average rate of formation of stars in the Galaxy
- ► the fraction of stars that have planets
- ► the number of planets each star might have where the environment is suitable for life
- ► the fraction of such planets where life actually does appear
- ► the fraction of *those* planets where life leads to the development of intelligence
- ► the fraction of civilizations that develop the ability and desire to communicate with others
- ► the average lifetime of such civilizations

Reading down this list, we find that we have less and less possibility of being able to produce adequate figures to slot into the equation. We have a rough idea (although we may be mistaken) of the rate at which new stars form; we suspect that many, if not most, of them have planets – and so on until we come to the question about how long our 'ideal' technological civilization might expect to endure, to which any answer must be the most unfounded of guesses. Furthermore, is it not overwhelmingly likely that there are other factors involved of which we know nothing, or which we simply overlook? It is hard to find any reason to ascribe the slightest scientific validity to the Green Bank formula.

The problem with any such guesstimate is that, of course, we are basing our calculations on a statistical sample

LEFT *A metallic meteorite discovered in Mexico. Such meteorites give us few clues as to the prevalence of life on other worlds; however, members of a different class of meteorites – the carbonaceous chondrites – contain organic chemicals, leading us to believe that the building blocks of life must be fairly commonplace.*

of one. If a newspaper commissioned a political poll based on the opinion of a single person it would immediately become a laughing-stock. Scientists attempting to calculate the number of extraterrestrial civilizations are in exactly the same position: the only evidence we have for life anywhere in the Universe is confined to this planet.

Or is it? Some meteorites betray traces of proteinoid globules, the precursors of living cells. There is a great deal of suspicion that these may simply be the products of biological contamination after the meteorites have landed; but, if this is not the case, it would seem that life is likely to be rife throughout the Universe. And that, of course, leads us back to the question: 'Where *are* they all?'

The question acquires a new relevance when we look at the propositions of some of the CETI theorists (CETI = Communication with ExtraTerrestrial Intelligence). The US scientist Ronald Bracewell seems to have been the first to have suggested that sending or listening for radio signals is a haphazard business and almost certainly doomed to failure, because the task of covering the millions of 'likely' stars is well-nigh impossible. He proposed that, instead, we should pepper the skies with computer-controlled probes. This would be an expensive and very long-term project, but sooner or later one of the probes would encounter an extraterrestrial civilization – assuming there are any – and communications could be set up.

The idea has been expanded, notably by the Scottish CETI theorist Chris Boyce. Sending out a sufficient number of Bracewell-style probes would be prohibitively expensive. However, if such probes were programmed so that, each time they encountered a planetary system, they located a suitable asteroid and from its raw materials built several replicas of themselves, which were then despatched to further stars, the chances of success would be staggeringly increased. Such von Neumann probes, as they have been dubbed – after the US mathematician John von Neumann (1903–57) – would obviously have to possess a more than rudimentary machine intelligence. The likelihood of their establishing contact with an extraterrestrial civilization would therefore be yet further increased, because probes emanating from different civilizations would, with luck, run across each other, exchange information, and in due course establish communications between their parent cultures.

This approach has been described by its supporters as the 'uniquely logical' method of attempting to establish CETI. Some scientists who think that there is little likelihood of there being any other technological civilization in the Galaxy agree that the approach is indeed 'uniquely logical' – and have gone on from there to support their own case. After all, they point out, if there were other civilizations, the asteroid belt of our own Solar System should be packed out with von Neumann probes. To this there is an instant response: it may be, but we don't know because we haven't looked. (Also, of course, if every civilization adopts that attitude, then none of them will send out von Neumann probes . . .)

If we cannot make any sensible estimates as to the existence of intelligence on other worlds, at least we can look at non-human intelligences back here on Earth. There are two categories to be considered: animals and machines.

When we assess animal intelligence we tend to take a very anthropocentric view; that is, our yardstick of a creature's intelligence is how closely it resembles our own. This is not a

LEFT *A fixed radio interferometer aerial, 440m long, at the Mullard Radio Astronomy Observatory, Cambridge, England.* **BELOW RIGHT** *A group of dolphins. Some scientists believe that these marine mammals may be more intelligent than human beings.*

Even when intelligence is measured in human terms, some animals show up rather well. A number of dolphins have been taught to communicate in rudimentary English. Their vocabularies are small, but even so the achievement is almost miraculous: how many human beings have learned to speak and understand dolphin-language? Chimps, whose vocal chords are not well adapted to human speech, have discovered how to communicate using deaf-and-dumb language; again, this is an incredible achievement. In both cases the limitations of vocabulary should not be seen necessarily to imply any lack of ability for abstract thought: these animals are using an alien tool to communicate with a species (us) whose intellectual make-up is quite alien to them, so it is hardly surprising that there are comparatively few areas of common ground that can be described using human words.

We can understand this more clearly if we imagine that the tables have been turned, and that we are trying to get by in basic dolphin-language. Dolphins have a sense which we do not have: using something akin to our sonar, they can 'see' their surroundings holographically (in true 3D, rather than the effect of 3D our stereoscopic vision creates). There are no words in any human language that can adequately describe the experience of 'seeing' something in this way –

useful approach, because it assumes that all forms of intelligence are of the same qualitative type. Any attempt to *quantify* the relative intelligences of species – and even of human beings from different cultural backgrounds – is quite patently misguided. one is trying to apply the same measure to two qualitatively different things. Even within the same culture, comparative tests of intelligence are on shaky ground; as has often been observed, all that IQ tests are good at measuring and demonstrating is the ability of individuals to pass IQ tests.

The point is not that we in any way deliberately do down the intelligence of animals – although we do this as well – but that it is hard for us to imagine the workings of forms of intelligence that have evolved to cope with environmental circumstances different from our own. The imperatives directing the evolution of intelligence differ between one species and the next. What is valuable to us, as a land-based animal, need not be valuable to a marine creature like a dolphin, and vice versa.

precisely because human beings do not have a holographic sense and so have never required the words to describe it nor the intellectual ability to be able to imagine it. (In exactly the same way, congenitally blind people can understand the physics of vision, but are unable to conceive what it would be like to experience seeing, for example, different colours. Helen Keller wrote very interestingly of her own conception of the different colours people described to her; the descriptions conjured up tactile sensations. She knew of the greenness of moss as 'velvety', the whiteness of lilies as 'soft'.)

How, then, can we evaluate animal intelligence? The answer is that we cannot, except in the vaguest of terms. There is little doubt that the average human being is more intelligent than the average cow – no contest! When it comes to comparisons with more overtly intelligent beasts – dolphins, whales, squids, chimps, gorillas, even rats – we cannot be so confident. None of these animals have the sort of intelligence that would enable them to function as successful human beings (ignoring the physical differences), but then we would not seem to have the kind of intelligence that would enable us to operate successfully in *their* environments.

Machine intelligence presents a slightly different case, because it is to a great extent governed by human intelligence: clearly, when we design an artificial brain, we create it in our own (intellectual) image. We expect it to be good at mathematics, particularly, and also at various other obvious human capabilities. However, we do not expect our computers to be capable of experiencing emotions, even though emotions are clearly a fundamental part of human intelligence. It is also a cliché that computers are incapable of creative thought – in other words, imagination.

BELOW *The computer centre at* CERN. RIGHT *The face of the future? A robot seals a seam at a car plant.*

This may change soon, though. Scientists talk in terms of 'generations' of computers, and the most advanced of the machines in operation at the moment are of the fourth generation. There is much speculation about the advent of fifth-generation machines which, it is proposed, will be capable of learning, extrapolation, ratiocination and imagination – and hence, possibly, of something that we would recognize as emotion. A science-fiction dream? Perhaps not. In the early 1980s a government-funded Japanese project was set up to develop a fifth-generation computer. The Japanese have a habit of scheduling their 'breakthroughs' in advance, which may seem silly but in practice generally works. The project predicted that their big breakthrough would come in 1990. Interestingly, the only doubts that Western scientists seemed to express about the viability of the project concerned this deadline.

Although the machine intelligences we create will be based on our own form of intelligence and an extension of it, we can nevertheless expect them to be alien in many ways. They will have senses beyond any that we can conceive. In a way, computers already do. For example, the simplest desktop computer functions through 'perceiving' shifting patterns of electrons, something which we cannot do because we are not aware of electrons in everyday life. Who knows what thoughts may pass through the mind of a machine capable of consciously perceiving such patterns, and *thinking* about them?

Does Intelligence Depend on Nature or Nurture?

Cyril Burt died in 1971. Throughout his lifetime he had been regarded as an excellently scientific psychologist who had shown that the level of a child's intelligence has little to do with the child's home environment; instead it is a product of the intelligences of the child's parents. Fairly good evidence has since appeared to show that Burt faked his results in order to bolster his case, although he still has some apologists.

The idea that a child's intelligence might depend solely on the intelligences of his or her parents seems commonsensical: all around us we see clever kids born of clever parents. However, the situation is not quite as clear-cut as it might seem. Clever parents are, naturally, going to give their children a more encouraging educational environment: to take a single example, they are not going to have the television set on at full volume while the unfortunate kids are attempting to do their school homework. It is now generally accepted that nurture – the environment in which a child grows up – is a more important factor than heredity when it comes to the intelligence of the resulting adult human being.

That nurture is more important than nature seems to be borne out by a study published in *Nature* in 1989. This showed that, on average, children adopted by high-earning

LEFT *The relationship between a child and both its parents, especially in the early years, seems to have a dominant effect on how well the child will be able to exploit her or his intelligence in later life.* **ABOVE RIGHT** *Television can be a powerful influence for education or, conversely, hinder it.* **FAR RIGHT** *The gift of reading is one of the most important a parent can give to a child.*

families had an IQ 12 points higher than similar children adopted by low-earning families – whatever the social class of the children's natural parents. Obviously it wasn't the money that made the difference: what was important was the fact that the wealth opened up all sorts of possibilities to the lucky children that simply were not available to adopted children of poorer parents.

The results of the survey are still controversial, so perhaps we should not allow them too much weight. Moreover, as Dr Matt McGue of the University of Minnesota commented at the time,

> ... WORKING-CLASS PARENTS CAN PROVIDE THEIR CHILDREN WITH INTELLECTUALLY STIMULATING EXPERIENCES AND PROFESSIONAL PARENTS CAN NEGLECT THE NEEDS OF THEIR CHILDREN ...

In other words, nurture is very important but heredity is probably significant, too. Or is that really true? We look at families like the Huxleys, the Darwins and the Russells and we begin to wonder.

One thought which throws a much-welcomed spanner in everyone's works is this: the parents of Einstein and Shakespeare were not noted for either their intelligence or their prosperity, yet their children seem to have done all right. In short, the whole debate about the relative contributions to a child's intelligence of upbringing and genetics is still wide open. It seems probable that a mixture of the two factors is involved, but we cannot be sure that this is the case and we most certainly cannot say which is more important than the other – let alone quantify (in terms of percentages) their relative importances.

We can, however, make a few generalizations. Book-oriented homes lead to book-oriented children: a child brought up in a home where reading is encouraged as a major activity is more likely to read voraciously from an early age. Such children may not be in fact more intelligent than their schoolmates, but certainly they are able to exploit more fully the intelligence which they do have, and possibly be better-informed. This is an advantage which they may continue to enjoy throughout life.

Is Immortality a Scientific Possibility?

The reasons for our mortality become obvious as soon as we stop thinking of ourselves as individuals. This is not a very palatable view: each of us likes to think that we are 'somebody special' – which is why each of us accepts intellectually that someday we must die but at a gut level believes that, in our own case, God, Fate or whatever will make an exception. However, if we look at the phenomenon of life in terms not of individuals but of the species as a whole, the necessity of personal death becomes obvious.

In order to survive, a species must be capable of adapting to changing circumstances. It can do so only through a constant turnover of individuals, whose sole purpose in being born is to reproduce and then die. Those products of reproduction – children – that are best adapted to the current circumstances will generally survive until they are of a suitable age to reproduce, passing on at least some of the characteristics favouring survival to their own children: those who are poorly adapted to the current circumstances will, in general, either die young or be unable to find a mate. Richard Dawkins has taken this idea further by suggesting that the sole purpose for human existence is to allow the further evolution of genes.

Evolution is generally regarded as a slow process, but in fact it works remarkably swiftly. To take a single example, it is reported that the grandchildren of the first European colonists of North America already had eyelid-shapes tending towards those of the Red Indians, which were better adapted to looking out over vast spaces in bright sunlight. Organisms simpler than human beings, like bacteria and viruses, mutate even more rapidly, because of both their simplicity and their rapid reproductive cycle.

Individual immortality would threaten the species as a whole – almost certainly with fatal results. If the immortals were capable of reproduction there would be a colossal population explosion: imagine what it would be like if every human being ever born were still alive! Alternatively, if the immortals were not capable of reproduction, their species would inevitably stagnate, be unable to adapt and in the end – through accident or otherwise – die out.

This is all very well, but most of us are interested in not general but *personal* immortality; others may come and go, but we ourselves, as individuals, would like to carry on living forever, please. Medical science – in particular, genetic engineering and spare-part surgery – is beginning to offer hopes of, if not immortality, then at least a major extension of lifespan. This may seem an attractive proposition, but in fact it is rather frightening – because it would be available only to some of us. We can conjecture immense social strife, as the 'haves' battle with the 'have-nots'. Similarly, it is reasonable to suppose that many of the haves will be among the most ruthless of society, and will pass on their inhumane ethic to their children, thereby perpetuating it: is this really the future we wish for our species?

A quite different way of extending humanity's average lifespan concerns genes and the age at which we reproduce. Most people are in their twenties or early thirties when they have children; the average age of first parenthood seems if anything to be falling. Any inbuilt coding – in the form of genes – that could affect us after our child-bearing period is irrelevant to the survival of the species: the genes involved might code us for death but, in terms of the species, this does not matter because we have already served our purpose by reproducing. Obviously the hypothetical 'death-genes' cannot come into action before later life. If, therefore, human beings as a whole progressively delayed the age at which they reproduced, the 'death-genes' would, over the course of the generations, be gradually filtered out – for the very simple reason that people most affected by 'death-genes' would die before reproducing, and hence would be unable to pass on the fatal genes to the next generation.

We must return to the fundamental question: is the extension of the human lifespan actually desirable? We already have a global population problem: do we really want to exacerbate it? Obviously not. Yet there is no reason – aside from short-sighted economics – why we should not increase our living area by creating new habitats for our species. These could be on other planets, in artificial space colonies or even beneath the Earth's own oceans. The possibilities are there: all we have to do is grasp them.

And, if we do, there are no external reasons why the average lifespan of all human beings should not be extended to many hundreds of years.

How Many Senses Are There?

The knee-jerk answer is that there are five; but, like most such answers, this one is wrong. In addition to the generally recognized senses of vision, hearing, touch, smell and taste, human beings are known to have an additional one, called proprioception or kinaesthesia, whereby we are aware of the relative position of our limbs, the tensions in our muscles and so on.

Clearly, psychics should talk about having 'a seventh sense' rather than the sixth! There has been a lot of debate, generally conducted outside scientific circles, about the possible existence of such a sense – or, to be more accurate, set of senses. We can term them collectively ESP (for Extra-Sensory Perception), thereby embracing the supposed abilities of telepathy, clairvoyance, precognition and so on. In so doing we are probably, assuming such abilities exist, mixing chalk with cheese: clairvoyance, for example, may have as little to do with precognition as vision has to do with touch. We do not yet have any way of knowing.

ABOVE *George Zirkle who, in the early 1930s, showed impressive scores in ESP experiments run by JB Rhine.*

LEFT *A 19th-century experiment intended to demonstrate the existence of telepathy. As we can see, there was very little 'science' involved in these experiments; they were treated rather like party tricks – which, almost certainly, they were.*

What scientific evidence have we for the existence of ESP? The sad answer is: very little, if any. Laboratory experiments carried out on the subject have proved, almost always, frustrating. Those that have seemed to indicate that ESP might be at work have generally later been discredited: either the subject of the experiment has been proven to be a charlatan or the experimental procedure itself has been shown to be flawed. For legal reasons it is impossible to mention examples of the former instance. As an example of the latter we can recall one case in which the famous 'scientific' investigator of the paranormal, JB Rhine (1895–1980), asked an experimental subject to try, clairvoyantly, to perceive the images on a set of cards that Rhine was turning up. At the time, Rhine was sitting in the front of his car while the subject was in the rear seat. However, Rhine was convinced that the astonishingly successful experiment showed a genuine result, because he had told the subject not to peek!

The scientific evidence may be lacking, but there is a colossal body of anecdotal evidence in favour of ESP – and there are few people who, in honesty, cannot recall one or more instances in which they themselves have had an experience which they can explain only in terms of it. The vast majority of such experiences can easily be interpreted in terms of orthodox science – usually statistics: most people, including myself, have only a hazy understanding of the workings of probability, and so perfectly commonplace coincidences seem to be outrageously improbable, and are therefore viewed as being in some way paranormal. Moreover, many widely reported accounts of astonishing experiences are elaborations or flat lies. Even so, some of the anecdotes cannot be so lightly dismissed. Out of the many examples available, here is one chosen more or less at random. It was recounted by Colin Wilson in *The Directory of Possibilities*:

JANE O'NEILL WITNESSED A SERIOUS ACCIDENT, AND WAS SO SHOCKED THAT SHE HAD TO TAKE SEVERAL WEEKS OFF WORK. AFTER THIS SHE HAD ODD FLASHES OF 'CLAIRVOYANCE'. ONE DAY, SHE VISITED THE CHURCH AT FOTHERINGHAY WITH A FRIEND AND WAS IMPRESSED BY A PICTURE BEHIND THE ALTAR. SHE MENTIONED IT LATER TO HER FRIEND, WHO SAID SHE HAD NOT SEEN THE PICTURE. LATER, TO SETTLE THE MATTER, THEY RETURNED TO THE CHURCH AND, TO O'NEILL'S SURPRISE, IT WAS A COMPLETELY DIFFERENT PLACE; IT WAS SMALLER, AND THE PICTURE WAS NOT THERE. SHE CORRESPONDED WITH AN EXPERT ON THE CHURCH, WHO TOLD HER THAT THE CHURCH SHE HAD 'SEEN' WAS THE CHURCH AS IT HAD BEEN 400 YEARS AGO, BEFORE IT HAD BEEN REBUILT IN 1553.

There is little reason to doubt O'Neill's honesty: clearly she had a very unusual experience. However, this does not necessarily mean that ESP was involved. As Wilson mentions, she had recently had a harrowing shock, so it is possible that she was hallucinating in some way and that, by chance, her hallucinations corresponded approximately with historical reality. Researchers into the paranormal would say, quite fairly, that such complicated explanations are actually more difficult to believe in than ESP. In this case, as in so many others, the truth is impossible to establish because the event was a personal one: the individual 'knows' what he or she experienced, but we can never, as it were, run through a tape-recording of the experience in order to try to establish what 'really' happened.

The existence or otherwise of ESP is one of the great mysteries of science, yet very few scientists show any interest

LEFT *Fotheringhay Church in Northamptonshire, England, where Jane O'Neill underwent what appeared to be a timeslip of four centuries.*

RIGHT *A telepathy experiment featuring a blindfolded Kuda Bux, who is reproducing the symbols drawn on the board by Lucie Kaye despite the fact that he cannot see them. Or can he? Most modern researchers into the paranormal set little store by such experiments.*

in it whatsoever. A major reason for this unconcern is that various fraudsters who have operated in the field have given ESP a bad name: underfunded scientists have far better things to investigate than a phenomenon which seems, on the basis of the available evidence, to be nothing more than a farrago. This is a pity, because the few scientists who have gone into the matter in rigorous detail have concluded that there at least *might* be something in it.

Certainly there is a lot of evidence that we have senses other than the 'official' six. Some people are always aware of the direction of north (as are migratory birds). A few people never need to wear a watch because they always know what the time is. Many of us find that we 'know' when we are being watched. Some people can 'feel' the presence nearby of massive objects; even if blindfolded they would run little risk of walking into a wall. An appreciable number of us have 'perfect pitch': we can identify a musical note exactly. All of us feel heat – we have a 'temperature sense'. The list could go on for a long time.

When we turn to the animal kingdom we discover a whole array of senses which we, as human beings, reckon we do *not* have. The use of sonar by bats, dolphins and others is a prime example: to describe it as merely an extension of the sense of hearing is simplistic, especially in the case of dolphins. Then there is the little understood sense possessed by certain fishes, whereby they can detect an object because of its minute electrical activity. Many organisms can 'see', at least fuzzily, using heat-sensitive cells – a handy ability for a night-time predator. This is another list that could go on for a long time.

In sum, there is no definitive answer to the question of how many senses there are: we have yet to discover all of our own, and even less do we know the full details of those enjoyed by some of the other members of the Animal Kingdom. There is even evidence that plants have senses, although we have no real conception of what those senses might be. The subject as a whole is a mystery for the reason which we touched on earlier in the context of ESP: we can never share another person's experiences. The same is true, but this time with a vengeance, when it comes to animals and plants. We can look at the way other creatures behave and from our observations infer the senses to which they are responding, but our inferences may be misleading us. For example, does an animal recoil from a naked flame because it can feel the heat or because it can 'see' the heat – or because it has some completely different sense that alerts it to the danger?

We do not know.

What Do Dreams Mean?

All of us dream. Some people believe that they do not dream; in fact they do, but they are unable to remember their dreams when they wake in the morning. Researchers have discovered that periods of dreaming during sleep are related to times of rapid-eye movement (REM) during which the eyes flick from side to side under the eyelids. You can see this happening if you watch someone asleep.

From earliest times it has been assumed that at least some dreams are important – bearing messages either from the gods or from the dreamer's subconscious, depending upon one's cultural context. These messages, it is widely believed, can give information about the future, the remote past or things taking place in distant parts of the world; at a more down-to-earth level, psychologists and especially psychoanalysts think that analysis of dreams can reveal details of a person's mental state, and have concocted numerous systems relating objects or events seen in dreams to aspects of the human psyche. Sex is the favourite topic: among the many symbols of sex are serpents, swords, running up a flight of stairs, swimming, flying . . . In fact, it is quite hard to think of a dream-image which cannot in some way be ingeniously linked to an aspect of the dreamer's sex-life, lack of it, or attitudes towards it.

All of us who recall our dreams recognize that they come in two different categories. These can be described as 'only' dreams and 'different' dreams. An 'only' dream has little effect on us; we may remember it in the morning because it was funny or for some other reason, but it does not disturb us in any way; most often, we recollect it only in the moments after waking and have forgotten it by the time we get out of bed. (An interesting way of countering this effect is to keep

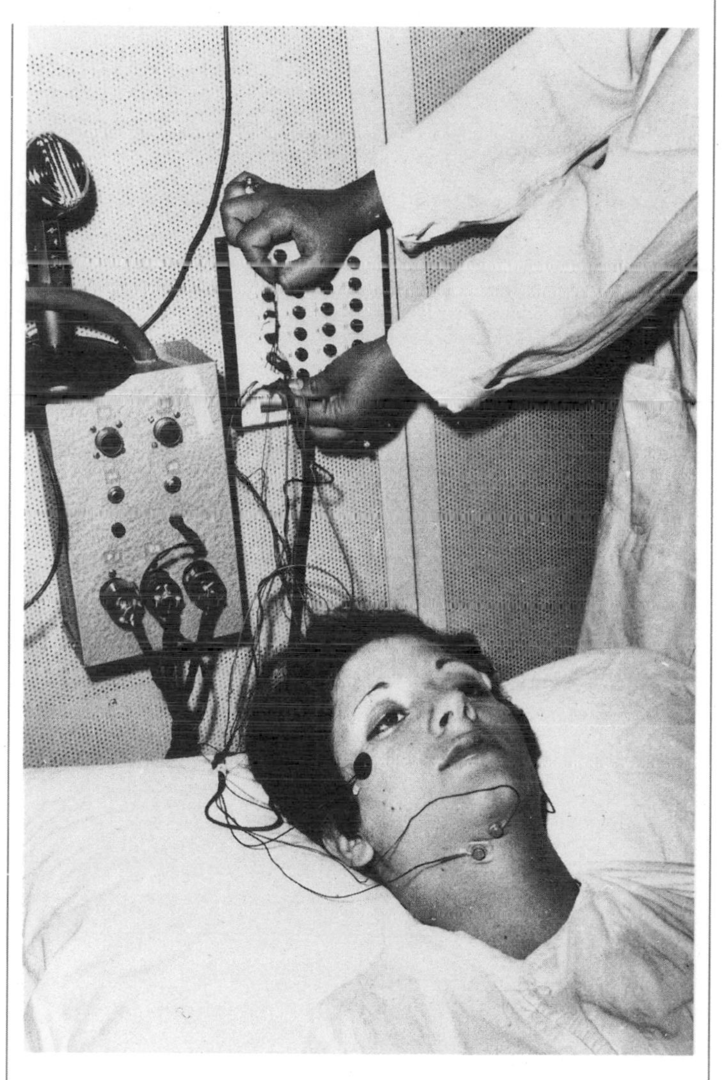

ABOVE *A dream-telepathy experiment being set up at Maimonides laboratory in Brooklyn, New York.*

LEFT *Robert Louis Stevenson and* ABOVE *Edgar Allan Poe, two writers who exploited their dreams to create works of imaginative fiction.*

by the bedside a 'dream diary' in which, as soon as you wake, you can jot down any memories you may have of your dreams. You will be surprised by how much more often you dream than you think you do.) A 'different' dream is a totally different beast from an 'only' dream. The prime example of a 'different' dream is a nightmare. Few of us are lucky enough to have escaped the shattering sensation of pure terror generated by nightmares: the experience can haunt our every action for days afterwards. But 'different' dreams need not necessarily be unpleasant; they affect our waking consciousness, certainly, but the effect may be one of pleasure rather than torment – as with a sexual dream. When people try to investigate the possible meanings of dreams, they focus on the 'different' dreams, regarding the 'only' dreams as just so much mental detritus.

It is possible that *all* dreams are merely mental detritus. This is not to say that dreams are unimportant. Far from it: a 'different' dream can profoundly influence the dreamer. What is being suggested is that dreams *in themselves* have no absolute meaning or import – so that the idea of analysing them in terms of standard sets of criteria becomes a nonsense – but that the reaction of the dreamer to his or her dream can be very significant. Imagine, for example, that two people have an identical dream – for the sake of argument we can conjecture that it concerns standing on an ants' nest. To one person this is an amusing fantasy, worth mentioning at the breakfast table, perhaps, but little more than that; to the other it is a horrific nightmare which lingers in the memory for days. The dream itself has no meaning; the effect it has on the second person tells a great deal about that person.

Nobody is yet sure what dreams actually are. We can describe them in terms of electrical activity in the brain, but this does not really tell us much. We all know, as dreamers, that dreams are genuine experiences, even if they cannot be recorded with a camera or a tape-recorder. Sometimes our dreams tell coherent stories, but more often they are a jumble that seems logical at the time but is revealed by our conscious memory as a nonsense. Some people experience 'lucid' dreams: they are aware, while dreaming, that that is exactly what they are doing, and in some cases can direct the course of the dream. Others dream when not fully asleep, either while waking (hypnopompic dreams) or while falling to sleep (hypnagogic dreams), and a few can do so lucidly – Edgar Allan Poe and Robert Louis Stevenson are two examples of writers who have gained inspiration through the use of lucid hypnagogic dreams.

We can look to one of Stevenson's non-lucid, non-hypnagogic dreams for a fine example of the way that daytime preoccupations can affect the dreaming mind, and vice versa. In his *Across the Plains* (1892) he wrote:

> I HAD LONG BEEN TRYING ... TO FIND A BODY, A VEHICLE, FOR THAT STRONG SENSE OF MAN'S DOUBLE-BEING WHICH MUST AT TIMES COME IN UPON AND OVERWHELM THE MIND OF EVERY THINKING CREATURE. I HAD EVEN WRITTEN ONE, *THE TRAVELLING COMPANION*, WHICH WAS RETURNED BY AN EDITOR ON THE PLEA THAT IT WAS A WORK OF GENIUS AND INDECENT, AND WHICH I BURNED THE OTHER DAY ON THE GROUND THAT IT WAS NOT A WORK OF GENIUS, AND THAT *JEKYLL* HAD SUPPLANTED IT. THEN CAME ONE OF THOSE FINANCIAL FLUCTUATIONS ... FOR TWO DAYS I WENT ABOUT RACKING MY BRAINS FOR A PLOT OF ANY SORT; AND ON THE SECOND NIGHT I DREAMED THE SCENE AT THE WINDOW, AND A SCENE AFTERWARD SPLIT IN TWO, IN WHICH HYDE, PURSUED FOR SOME CRIME, TOOK THE POWDER AND UNDERWENT THE CHANGE IN THE PRESENCE OF HIS PURSUERS. ALL THE REST WAS MADE AWAKE, AND CONSCIOUSLY ... ALL THAT WAS GIVEN ME WAS THE MATTER OF THREE SCENES, AND THE CENTRAL IDEA OF A VOLUNTARY CHANGE BECOMING INVOLUNTARY.

Here we can see the two-way exchange between waking consciousness and dream-consciousness. Stevenson was deliberately seeking a plot that would allow him to explore an aspect of human psychology. It would seem reasonable to suggest that it was this waking preoccupation of his that caused his subconscious to produce the relevant dream. However, we can turn this line of reasoning on its head. Had he had the same nightmare at any other time, it might have had no particular meaning to him at all. *Any* 'different' dream he had around that time might have served to give him the 'vehicle' he was seeking. The 'meaning' of the dream seems therefore not to have been implicit in the dream itself but to have come from the interaction between its imagery and Stevenson's consciously controlled imagination – 'All the rest was made awake ...'

There are various current theories which attempt to explain the phenomenon of dreaming. None are particularly satisfactory and all seem to be unprovable. They are worth mentioning here only because they are interesting. One idea is that we pick up all sorts of information during our waking hours without being consciously aware that we are doing so; the function of dreaming is to allow our brain to process all this information at the unconscious level. Another, closely related, hypothesis is that at the end of each day we have in our unconscious a sort of ragbag of bits and pieces of experience which our conscious mind has not had the time, opportunity or inclination to process; once again, the function of the dream is to deal with this material. A different notion concerns wish-fulfilment: in our dreams we can do with impunity things we would like to do in real life but cannot – make love with a Hollywood sex symbol or murder our boss. This is a very appealing theory but scarcely seems to be borne out by the facts; after all, we dream about all sorts of things which in no way do we wish to experience in real life. A very prosaic theory proposes that the electrical activity of the brain as we sleep produces the mental equivalent of white noise and that, just as we can make ourselves hear music in white noise, our unconscious can pick out a coherent story from the baffling array of visual images presented to it. Less scientific explanations of dreaming include messages from the gods, the ability of the spirit/soul to travel outside the body during sleep, and so on.

Dreaming does not seem to be confined to our own species: research on the subject would appear to indicate that animals likewise have dreams: we have all seen a sleeping dog twitch as it 'chases rabbits'. Charles Darwin, in *The Descent of Man* (1871), wrote about the matter:

AS DOGS, CATS, HORSES, AND PROBABLY ALL THE HIGHER ANIMALS, EVEN BIRDS, HAVE VIVID DREAMS, AND THIS IS SHEWN BY THEIR MOVEMENTS AND THE SOUNDS UTTERED," WE MUST ADMIT THAT THEY POSSESS SOME POWER OF IMAGINATION. THERE MUST BE SOMETHING SPECIAL, WHICH CAUSES DOGS TO HOWL IN THE NIGHT, AND ESPECIALLY DURING MOONLIGHT, IN THAT REMARKABLE AND MELANCHOLY MANNER CALLED BAYING.

ABOVE *One of William Hole's illustrations for Stevenson's* Dr Jekyll and Mr Hyde, *probably the most famous of all dream fictions.*

Darwin was, of course, indulging in a piece of speculation. More recent studies have shown that at least the higher primates display REM while sleeping, and therefore probably do dream. As to what their, and our, dreams mean – that is a matter of sheer guesswork. As I have written in another context (*Dreamers*, 1984), 'Humanity is going to look pretty silly if it turns out that dreams don't mean anything at all.'

What Determines a Child's First Words?

LEFT *Sunset in the Seychelles, a scene of tranquillity that inspires tranquillity in the viewer.* ABOVE *Another scene in the Seychelles, this time offering us tranquillity for very different reasons; the rocks and the overshadowing branches indicate to us that here we can enjoy good observation of our surrounds without ourselves being observed.*

One of the oddities of child development is that the word meaning 'mother' is so similar in so many languages. That the Sanskrit *matr* should give rise to the Greek *meter* and hence the Latin *mater* may seem hardly a surprise, since each of these languages influenced its successor. What is less easy to explain is that all of these words seem to have been created as phonetic imitations of the first meaningful sound uttered by many babies. This sound begins with the enunciation of the letter 'm', and can be variously 'mama', 'mummy', 'maman', 'mutta', 'maaa' and so forth; the feature of the baby's environment designated by the word is almost invariably the mother. The reason for this trans-cultural similarity of language is not known; it may simply be that 'm' is the easiest of all the consonants to produce.

Some babies ignore the 'rules'. They may decline for some quite considerable time to use any particular sound to indicate their mother, instead preferring to fix on some other aspect of their environment. My own child's first 'word' was 'doidledoidledaddy', a fact that rightly infuriated her mother. Other children can pick on such ephemera as 'toaster', 'video' and 'potty'.

This points up a second mystery. It is easy enough to accept that a child's first word should label its mother, until we start to think about it: why should a child connect sounds with objects at all? There is no obvious reason. After all, the relationship is a fairly remote one: the young child equates a sequence of consonants and vowels with a physical object, which is by no means an obvious connection. The baby could simply point, which is what quite a number of them do.

The riddles of babies' first words have yet to be solved. At present little research is being done on the subject.

How Common Is Cannibalism?

The eating of human flesh and the drinking of human blood in order to absorb the qualities of the deceased are practices which seem to date back as far as humankind itself. The Judaeo-Christian tradition regards cannibalism as a sin, but other major religions beg to disagree, on the grounds that, if a person is dead already, the consumption of his or her body is not going to make much difference. During the Middle Ages Christian countries took this idea one step further: drinking the blood of a just-beheaded criminal was widely regarded as an effective cure for epilepsy, and mixtures containing powdered human bones and/or flesh were popularly regarded as aphrodisiacs.

That drinking human blood can increase fertility is an old idea. It is related that Annia Galeria Faustina, the wife of the Roman Emperor Marcus Aurelius (121–180), was so desperate to become pregnant that she drank the warm blood of a dead gladiator. Her son became the Emperor Commodus, one of the nastiest Roman rulers of all. Clearly it would be unscientific to make any connection between Annia's and Commodus's different versions of bloodthirstiness!

The practice of eating dead enemies probably arose from the idea that you could absorb the better qualities of the person who had died through eating their flesh. Conversely, eating the person's body might indicate the ultimate contempt, in that you were degrading them completely: as you ate parts of the body you were mocking the person's erstwhile vigour and simultaneously stealing it for your own use. A couple of examples are worth noting. As recently as 1971 a member of the Black September organization boasted proudly of drinking the blood of the assassinated Wasfi Tal. Later in the 1970s Idi Amin, then dictator of Uganda, was

LEFT AND RIGHT *Two famous figures reputed to have indulged in cannibalism, Annia Galeria Faustina and (pointing) Idi Amin, one-time dictator of Uganda.*

accused of eating parts of the human beings who, indubitably, died in his torture camps.

Did any of this happen?

The evidence is remarkably elusive. A 1979 article ('The Man-Eating Myth') by Professor W Arens, surveys a wide range of cannibalism stories concerning the Caribbean, South America, New Guinea and West Africa, and finds that every account is based on hearsay rather than eye-witness reports. His conclusion is that tales of cannibalism have yet to be proved – they are travellers' tales rather than anything else. Even if we agree with his general hypothesis, we have to accept that in some instances people will eat the dead bodies of other people – if only in order to stay alive.

The conclusion to which we can come is that cannnibalism is rare but that, *in extremis*, it is something to which the human species will resort.

Why Are Human Beings Monogamous?

Humans are not the only animals to display the habit known as pair-bonding – the practice whereby parents stay together throughout the time that their offspring require to attain adulthood. Yet there is something of a mystery in this connection. Human males are capable of fertilizing almost as many human females as they would wish; some of our close relations among the higher primates do exactly that. Among the primates it seems that the identity of the mother is important; that of the father is irrelevant. (The role of males in baboon tribes provides an interesting exception to the general rule.) Yet human parents generally stay together until their offspring are fully grown – and may even cohabit until the end of their lives despite the fact that they bear no more offspring together.

The reasons for this are very far from clear. In part they seem to be societal – you score no points if you ditch your spouse – but largely they seem to concern the very basic matter of pair-bonding. This ignores the fact that some men and some women wish to encounter as many sexual partners as possible, behaviour which may have good biological reasons behind it. It seems unlikely that monogamy is a natural state for the human animal.

PART THREE

MYSTERIES OF THE UNIVERSE

All mysteries of science are, by definition, mysteries of the Universe, which, for the sake of argument, we can say is the sum total of all matter, all energy, and all events that have taken place throughout past time and will take place throughout future time. In this part of the book we shall consider mysteries on the grand scale – and also on the inconceivably tiny. At one moment we shall be talking in terms of billions of years and billions of light years; at the next we shall focus on events that are of importance for only billionths of a second involving particles so small that it is misleading to think of them as material objects.

There is no paradox in this. Those tiny events and particles mould the Universe as a whole. Stars could not shine were it not for particles – called neutrinos – that are so insubstantial that they have no mass at all and can travel right through a solid object like the Earth as if it simply did not exist. And the birth of the Universe, if some current theories are to be believed, depended on particles that did not have any physical existence at all.

LEFT *Fred Hoyle in 1955, some years before he, Bondi and Gold propounded the Steady State Theory of the Universe. Hoyle, still active today, has never been scared of iconoclasm.*

How Did the Universe Come into Existence?

A few decades ago this would have been a much more controversial question than it is today, because one possible answer would have been that the Universe had always existed, and always would. This was because of a cosmological theory that was then very popular – the Steady State Theory propounded by the US scientist Thomas Gold and the UK scientists Hermann Bondi and Fred Hoyle.

One of the conundra of the Universe is that galaxies – vast islands composed of millions or billions of stars – are almost without exception receding from each other. We can tell this because the light from their stars is reddened, in the same way and for the same reasons as the noise of an ambulance siren or a car engine seems to change pitch downwards as the vehicle passes you. In whatever direction we look, the

LEFT Radiotelescopy has allowed us to examine the most remote areas of the Universe and determine the details of celestial objects that are so distant that they are invisible to optical telescopes. This is one of the instruments at the Nuffield Radio Astronomy Observatories, Jodrell Bank, England.

RIGHT *The pioneer of radioastronomy, Karl Jansky, with his directional radio aerial system, the precursor of modern radiotelescopes.* OPPOSITE PAGE *Antimatter particles were predicted before there was any hard evidence that they existed. In this photograph from CERN we see the annihilation of an antiproton in the 80cm Saday liquid-hydrogen bubble chamber.*

light from the galaxies shows this redshift; moreover, the more distant a galaxy, the greater its redshift. Some of the nearest galaxies are moving very slowly towards us (that is, the light from them shows a blueshift) but that is a purely local effect. The clear inference is that the Universe as a whole is expanding.

The obvious conclusion is that, at some moment in the far past, the Universe was compacted into a very small volume – the 'cosmic egg' – and then exploded in a 'Big Bang'. Gold, Bondi and Hoyle disagreed. They were reluctant to believe that there could ever have been a time when the Universe had not looked much like it is today. Also, the Big Bang Theory implied that the Universe had a finite extent – it had an 'outside' as well as an inside – and this was another idea that they could not stomach. They therefore proposed the idea of *continuous creation*, whereby matter was constantly popping into existence. The emergence of this matter would be sufficient to, as it were, 'push apart' the galaxies. Not very much new matter was required: Hoyle pointed out that, throughout the Universe, the appearance of a single hydrogen atom each century in a volume equal to that of the Empire State Building would be quite enough.

Unfortunately for the Steady State Theory, in 1965 two US electronics experts, Arno Penzias and Robert Wilson, detected a residual background microwave radiation present throughout the Universe. The only possible explanation of this radiation, which corresponds to a temperature of about 3K (3 C° above the absolute zero of cold), seemed to be that it represented the residual energy left over from the Big Bang. The Steady State Theory floundered on for a few more years, being continually revised, but eventually its three proponents conceded defeat.

However, the idea of the 'cosmic egg' was in itself not very satisfactory. If the 'egg' had existed for all eternity, why should it suddenly decide to explode? Conversely, if the egg had just popped into existence and then exploded, what could explain this bizarre event? Clearly there were as many flaws in the current version of the Big Bang Theory as there had been in the Steady State Theory. Another question troubled cosmologists' minds. Was the Big Bang a unique event? Was the Universe destined to go on expanding forever, or might it be that gravity would eventually pull all the galaxies back together again until there was a 'Big Crunch' – later to be followed by a new Big Bang? This mystery has yet to be solved, although two quite separate sets of theories seem to indicate that indeed there are successive Big Bangs.

Our modern ideas of what caused the Big Bang seem almost mystical. In order to grope towards an understanding of them we have to grasp the abstruse notion of the *particle sea*. This idea was born out of the theories of the brilliant British physicist Paul Dirac, who as long ago as 1930 proposed that there must be an analogue of matter called *antimatter*. To take a simple example, the important subatomic particle called the electron has a negative electrical charge. Dirac worked out mathematical equations that indicated that there ought to be a counterpart to the electron but having a positive electrical charge. Soon afterwards exactly such a particle – the antielectron, or positron – was detected, and we now know that for every type of particle there is an appropriate *antiparticle*.

In the same way that matter is constituted of fundamental particles, antiparticles are the building blocks of antimatter. However, matter and antimatter annihilate each other completely when they come into contact: an 'antimatter bomb' would create an explosion giving off such stupendous amounts of energy that the H-bomb would pale by comparison. It is thought possible that, when the Universe came into existence, there was by chance a little more matter than antimatter; most of the matter destroyed itself by interaction with the antimatter, but that still left some over – the matter which makes up the Universe around us. (It is possible that there may be areas of the Universe where antimatter galaxies, stars, planets and even life exist, but we have no evidence of this.)

How do these ideas relate to that of the particle sea? The suggestion is that the whole of the Universe is filled with *virtual particles*. In the simplest terms, these can be thought of as particles which at the moment do not in fact exist – but one day might. Just as a particle and an antiparticle will totally annihilate each other if placed in contact, there is no reason why pairs of particles and antiparticles cannot abruptly spring into existence – the accent being on the word 'pairs'. Because the particle and antiparticle in effect cancel each other out, their appearance together does not violate the laws of physics. Of course, almost always the two immediately annihilate each other, so the event might never have happened, but it is possible that on occasion, for one reason or another, the two are separated so swiftly that annihilation does not occur. Experiments have shown that these virtual particles are indeed present, although we cannot detect them directly.

We can imagine, then, a circumstance in which there were no such things as matter, antimatter or energy – only a sea of virtual particles. There were would be no such thing as *time*, either, in this situation, because for time to exist there must be events. All that is needed to disrupt this state of affairs is for a 'seed' to be planted. Perhaps some particles spontaneously emerged. The effect would spread like wildfire – but with a ferocity and energy release that no wildfire could ever match. There would be a colossal explosion – in other words, a Big Bang.

It must be stressed that this is only a possibility (and that the explanation has been very much simplified), but more and more researches are showing that it probably approximates to the truth. The precise circumstances of the birth of the Universe, perhaps some 15 billion years ago, are still a mystery – and are likely to remain so for many years.

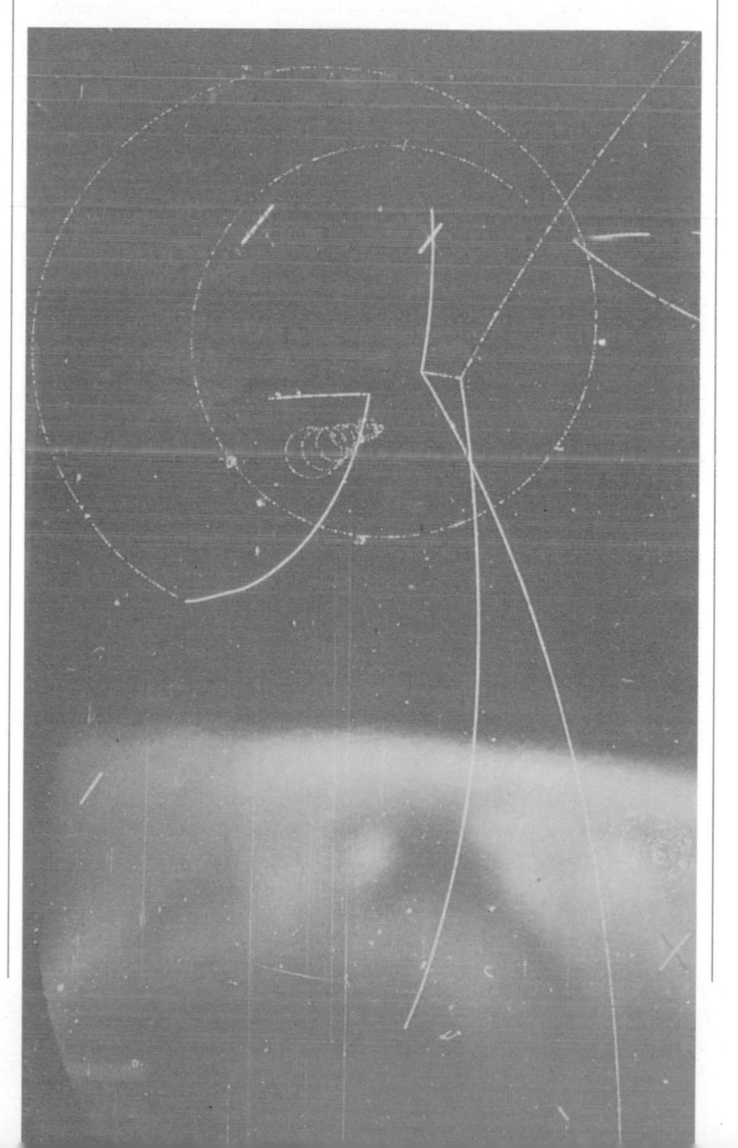

Could There be Many 'Little Bangs'?

According to the accepted theory, then, there was no such thing as time before the Big Bang. The explosion was not a simple three-dimensional one. Rather, it occurred in four dimensions: the three to which we are accustomed, plus time. In fact, the event was even more profound than that, because it was also an explosion *of* the four dimensions (as well as, it is thought, a number of others, which almost immediately 'rolled themselves up' so that we do not recognize them as such) – the matter and energy involved being only a secondary consideration! In a very real sense, then, the Big Bang Universe has existed forever.

Some scientists – and we should add hastily that they are in a small minority – feel that this is mincing words: they feel that by 'forever' we should mean an infinite number of billions of years rather than a period whose duration can be estimated. They are unhappy with the idea of a Universe that has not existed infinitely looking much the same as it does today – the same consideration which fuelled the Steady State Theory. This leaves the problem of how to explain the microwave background radiation.

One suggestion has been that perhaps the matter and energy of the Universe are brought into existence by an infinite series of 'Little Bangs'. These are events similar to the Big Bang but on a far smaller scale. Their cumulative effect would give rise to the microwave background radiation. The idea can also be used to explain the fact that the galaxies are all receding from each other because, just like the Big Bang, the 'Little Bangs' create not space (and trivia like matter and energy) but *spacetime*.

Here we need to pause to think about what we mean by spacetime. We all know that we exist in three dimensions – our bodies occupy a certain volume, and we can move it from one place to another. We know, too, that we exist in the fourth dimension, time, because we live for a certain number of years; besides, the fact that we can move in three dimensions implies our existence in the fourth, because movement requires time. That we think of this fourth-dimensional aspect of our lives as being in a different 'category' from the rest is really a matter of perception rather than reality. In order to define completely where you are right now you would need to use four mathematical coordinates, not three, and each of these would have exactly the same status as the rest. In terms of where you are relative to the Earth's surface, the four coordinates could be:

- latitude
- longitude
- altitude
- time

In short, we can see that we do not exist separately in space and time but in spacetime – and the same is true of everything else in the Universe.

Discussions involving spacetime inevitably turn to three-dimensional analogies: it should always be borne in mind that these are simplifications. Let us take a balloon as our model of the Universe, and its surface as representing spacetime. As we blow up the balloon, its surface gets larger (that is, spacetime expands). If we glued little pictures of galaxies to the surface, we would see that they moved progressively further apart as we inflated the balloon. The energy source powering this expansion is, of course, our breath.

TOP *The cluster of galaxies in Fornax.* **ABOVE** *The spiral galaxy* NGC 6946. *Here we can see both spiral and elliptical galaxies.* **LEFT** *The core of the nearest major galaxy to our own, the* Andromeda *Galaxy* M31.

LEFT *The Sombrero Hat Galaxy, one of the prettiest spirals.*

But there are two ways of blowing up a balloon. The ideal way is with a single, long exhalation, but most of us do not have the lung-power for that. We use a succession of shorter puffs – and here we get back to the 'Little Bangs'. The expansion of spacetime can be explained just as reasonably by the effects of a series of 'Little Bangs' as by that of a single Big Bang. The Universe would therefore have an infinite extent in all four dimensions of spacetime; it would always have existed, rather than having a moment of birth.

This is all very well, but even a 'Little Bang' should be a pretty spectacular affair. Yet, if we try to find one, we search the heavens in vain. For a while supporters of the theory placed great faith in quasars – very distant galaxies whose cores are giving off colossal amounts of energy. However, we now know that quasars are not 'Little Bangs' in progress.

Of course, 'Little Bangs' would necessarily be widely separated, so it is perfectly possible that there simply aren't any near enough to us to be detected: in an infinite Universe, our local patch – vast though that volume of space might seem to us to be – would be very small indeed.

The 'Little Bang' Theory cannot be completely dismissed, but it is today generally discounted. The problem is that, the further one goes into it, the more involved the science and mathematics become, with new rules and caveats having to be brought in to explain away apparent discrepancies. The Big Bang Theory, which is anyway much simpler, explains phenomena rather than, conversely, requiring postulated phenomena in order to explain it, and therefore must be for the moment preferred – although elsewhere we shall consider a variant of the 'Little Bang' Theory.

Do White Holes Exist?

If – and it is a very big 'if' – the matter sucked into a black hole must reappear somewhere and somewhen else, we must ask ourselves what the other end of the 'tunnel' would be like. Assuming that the 'outlet' is localized, it would be a site where raw energy gushed out into the Universe as if from nowhere. This energy would be in a complete mixture of forms, from long radio waves through light to highly energetic X-rays. Some of it might even be, at least briefly, in the form of matter, since matter and energy are interchangeable. Such a hypothetical 'outlet' is called a white hole, and in simplest terms is the opposite of a black hole.

If white holes exist they would seem to provide, in conjunction with their corresponding black holes, a rather neat way for the Universe constantly to replenish itself. Anything lost into a black hole would, at some time or another, be returned via a white hole. Moreover, white holes, by acting as conduits to bring new material and spacetime into new regions of the Universe, would act in rather the same way as 'Little Bangs', at least on the local level (the 'locality', of course, being extremely large). The influx of energy would help explain the microwave background radiation.

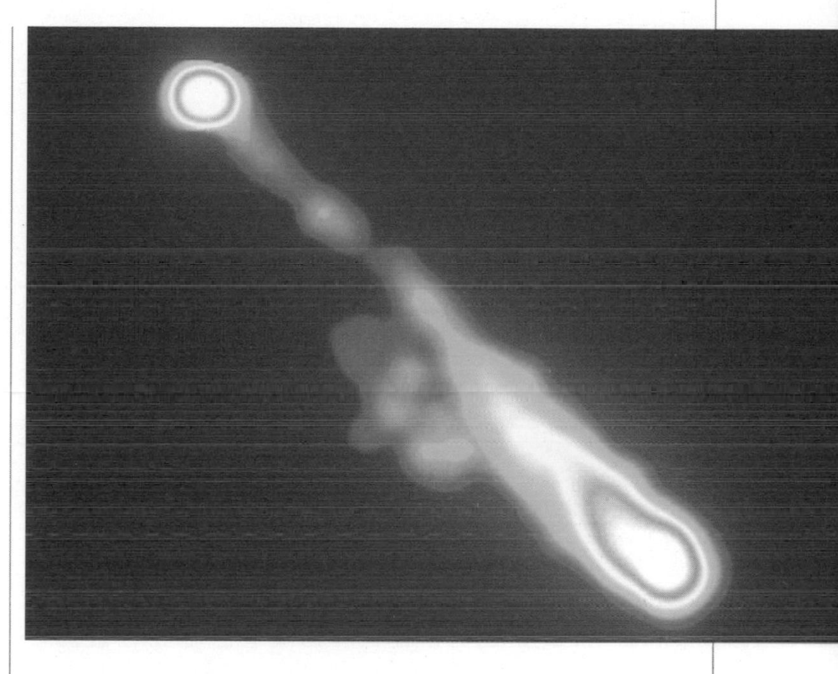

However, we have the same problem as with 'Little Bangs': white holes should be extremely obvious cosmic phenomena, broadcasting powerfully in every region of the energy spectrum, and yet we can find no trace of them. People have looked with interest but in vain at the cores of quasars, but they are certainly not white holes. In short, we still have no direct evidence that white holes exist.

There is a conundrum here. It is as certain as most things in astronomy can be that black holes exist – and are, indeed, common. They are predicted by theoretical physics, and there is good experimental evidence in favour of their existence. But the same theoretical physics predicts white holes, and yet we have no experimental evidence in favour of what should be far more obvious objects. Could it be that the Universe's first white holes have yet to form? Could it be that our assumption that matter and energy are returned to the Universe in discrete regions is wrong, that in fact they are returned piecemeal all over the Universe? Or could it simply be that the theory is grossly at fault?

This last might seem to be the most likely possibility but, if so, we are presented with yet another mystery: how can a theory which works so well for black holes not work equally well for their direct counterparts, white holes?

How Will the Universe Die?

If the ideas of those scientists who believe in an eternal Universe are correct, then of course the Universe will never die. However, it seems more likely that our Universe

- was born at a particular moment (the Big Bang)
- is currently evolving
- will continue to evolve in the future, and therefore
- cannot exist in its current form forever

The future fate of the Universe is not one of humanity's more pressing problems: on this scale nothing drastic is likely to happen for a few hundred billion years yet. (Much more worrying is that one of the nearby stars – notably Sirius or Procyon – could explode as a supernova, bathing our planet in sufficient hard radiation to extinguish all life. This should not happen for at least a million years ... but there is an outside chance that it could happen tomorrow.) Nevertheless, if we are to try to understand how the Universe works, we should pay as much attention to its death as to its birth.

Ideas of how the Universe will die vary from one scientific theory to the next. If we assume an ever-expanding Universe in which black holes already exist, then there is no question but that, in due course, all of the matter, energy and spacetime will be swallowed by the holes. Any small amounts of matter leaking from the black holes will gather together to form new stars, but those stars will themselves evolve until they either become black holes or are subsumed into black holes. The net result is a comparatively small number of supermassive black holes – perhaps only one.

Black holes are almost immortal, but not quite. These supermassive black holes will eventually 'evaporate' through their release of radiation. This radiation will be of the lowest possible grade – in other words, heat (hence the famous term 'heat death of the Universe'). At the same time, spacetime itself will break up; as matter and energy cannot exist without spacetime as a 'basis', the end product of this process can be nothing but – nothing.

Yes, but what do we mean by 'nothing'? In fact, what we have as the end-point of the heat death of the Universe is a timeless sea of virtual particles. This may seem familiar – as indeed it should, because we have discussed the particle sea in a rather different context: as the state of existence 'before' the Big Bang. From the heat death of our Universe we can therefore expect another universe to spring.

However, our Universe may not expand forever. The galaxies may continue to recede from each other but, under the influence of the Universe's own gravity, begin to slow down and then start to come towards each other again – in exactly the same way, and for exactly the same reason, that a ball thrown into the air will slow and then return to the ground. This view is known as the Oscillating Universe Theory. It implies that the following sequence occurs:

- a Big Bang
- expansion
- contraction, when gravity eventually overcomes expansion
- a 'Big Crunch' as all the matter in the Universe converges to a single point
- another Big Bang

The crucial question here is this: how much matter does the Universe contain? If there is less than a certain amount, the

LEFT *An artist's impression of our Galaxy, a typical spiral. There are billions of galaxies much like it in the Universe.*

gravitational force will be insufficient to stop a never-ending expansion. If there is more than a certain amount, gravity will in due course draw the galaxies back together.

Estimating the mass of all the matter in the Universe is not an easy task but, in the past few years, many scientists have devoted a great deal of time to it. Until quite recently it seemed quite certain (from estimates of stars' masses, interstellar dust, etc.) that the Universe would continue to expand until it met its heat death. Then cosmologists began to revise their estimates of the percentage of the Universe's mass made up by 'dark matter' which could not be directly observed – including black holes and pulsars. Almost overnight, the generally accepted opinion became that the Universe does indeed oscillate.

This notion has various interesting consequences. First, it implies that our Universe is only one of a never-ending succession. This is not too frightening an idea: we have already come across it in terms of the ever-expanding Universe.

Second, it demands that we think about the direction of time. We are accustomed to the 'arrow of time' pointing in a single direction: from past through present to future. In a shrinking Universe the opposite would presumably would be the case: the 'arrow' would go from future through present to past. This is not to say that history would repeat itself backwards: you would not die and then become old, middle-aged and youthful before finally being absorbed into your mother's womb. Much more alarming is the idea that you could not tell the difference between an expanding and a contracting Universe, and might indeed live in a Universe in which the arrow of time points in the opposite direction from the one you think it does! Such a scenario implies that you 'forget' more and more of the future and 'predict' the past much better. (The tenses are, of course, used loosely.)

A third possibility born from the idea of the oscillating Universe is that there is only a certain 'chunk' of time in which the whole succession of universes can exist. (It is much easier to imagine a single 'chunk' of space in which all possible universes can exist; but we must remember that time is a dimension just like the other three.) This implies that a vast number of universes coexist with our own, each having equal reality. This calls us back to the ideas of alternate universes which we were discussing earlier.

Can Anything Travel Faster Than Light?

Einstein's Theories of Relativity are generally assumed to tell us that nothing can travel faster than light. In fact, this is not what they say. Rather, they imply that to accelerate any material object up to and beyond light-speed would take an infinite amount of energy and would therefore be impossible. However, they also imply that there could be objects that have *always* travelled at faster-than-light speeds. For such particles, tachyons, infinite energy would be required to *slow them down* to light-speed. Their natural state would be movement at infinite velocity, so that they would be everywhere in the Universe at once.

Everything around us is, by contrast, a tardyon: it is inhibited by the velocity of light. The velocity of light can therefore be seen as a sort of barrier between the Universe we recognize and whatever unimaginable tachyonic universe there might be. This barrier seems to be impermeable: it is unlikely that we shall ever be able directly to detect tachyons (although there are some interesting ideas floating about concerning the consequences were we able to).

Tachyons, if they exist, have some intriguing properties. Perhaps the most interesting is that their time must run in the opposite direction to our own: their 'future' is the birth of the Universe and their 'past' is its end. If future technological societies ever learn to harness tachyons and modulate them (in the same way that we modulate radio waves) they will be able to communicate information from the future to the past. This breaking-down of the time barrier could be extremely exciting; at the same time, the very idea introduces so many paradoxes (if you communicate with the past you change it; you therefore change the present; therefore, in this new present, you never communicated with the past) that we

ABOVE *The young Albert Einstein.*

must think it unlikely that people will ever be able to use tachyons in this way ... unless communications were flitting between alternate universes, the existence of which would imply the simultaneous reality of all possibilities.

Conversely, these paradoxes may prove to be matters more of perception than of reality. If we imagine ourselves to be standing outside time, looking down upon the history of the Universe as if it were a relief map, we get a different perspective. The future is not interfering with the past; instead, it is fulfilling its obligations, as it were, by bringing about events that have already been reported. In fact, we can turn the apparent paradox on its head: what would happen if the people of the future decided *not* to communicate with the past, despite the fact that their histories told them that they were going to?

Looking at the time-reversal paradoxes again, we see that what they are really referring to is *information*, rather than particles. An individual tachyon whizzing backwards through time is not going to have any discernible effect on the past: it would be only when streams of them were encoded and transmitted to hypothetical 'tachyon detectors' that the paradoxes would begin. The same relationship exists between particles and information when we come to talk about the velocity of light in general. It is easy enough to send information *at* the speed of light: after all, we do exactly this when we wave at a friend or, to be more subtle, use any form of sign language. For theoretical reasons, however, any information sent at a velocity faster than that of light will cause paradoxes similar to those encountered when considering time-reversal. This aspect of Relativity is difficult fully to understand, but in simplest terms we can say that it is impossible to consider whatever is happening at this moment on α Centauri, about 4.5 lightyears away, as sharing a 'now' with whatever is happening here. The 'now' here instead corresponds to the 'now' on α Centauri in 4.5 years' time, because that is how long it takes light to get from here to there. If information could be transmitted from here to α Centauri in less time than this, it would effectively be travelling back into the past.

RIGHT *A photograph of part of the planet* Neptune *taken in* August 1989 *by* Voyager 2, *showing the linear cloud forms.*

A final point to note is that laboratory experiments have confirmed the results of various thought experiments concerning the way that photons behave when they encounter polarizing screens (which, like polaroid sunglasses, allow only photons 'wiggling' in a certain orientation to pass through). The results would seem to confirm that, at least at this level, information *can* be communicated at faster-than-light velocities – instantaneously, in fact. We may have to review exactly what we mean by the word 'paradox' – and, at the same time, rewrite many of our ideas of logic.

Does a Black Hole Orbit the Sun?

Percival Lowell (1855-1916) was not an orthodox astronomer. He was convinced that the surface of the planet Mars was criss-crossed by irrigational canals, betraying the presence on that world of a sophisticated civilization. He was not the first to have been deceived by flaws of telescopic lenses. His other *idée fixe* was, however, a little more rational. At the time it was known that the Sun's retinue consisted of eight planets. The orbit of the outermost of these, Neptune, showed perturbations ('wobbles'), indicating that there was a ninth planet. Lowell instituted a search for this unknown planet, confidently predicting exactly where it should be. His instinct was much better than his maths: some 13 years after his death the planet Pluto was discovered in 1930 by Clyde Tombaugh, using a mixture of perseverance and chance.

There was a mystery, however. Pluto (since discovered to be a 'double planet') is far too small to create the perturbations in Neptune's orbit that started off the search in the first place. The immediate reaction was that the discovery of Pluto was nothing more than a small-scale diversion: there must be a *tenth* planet out there, and a very large planet at that. The search for such a planet has proved unsuccessful – which is something of a mystery, because a planet of that size should be reasonably easy to find. Assuming, that is, that its orbit is not anomalous: one intriguing notion has been that the tenth planet does not orbit the Sun in the same plane as all the others; instead it goes 'up and over'. (Some quite eminent astronomers support this theory.)

However, the Universe is in many ways a very orderly place: if nine planets orbit a star in roughly the same plane, the tenth can be expected to do likewise. Various scientists have therefore proposed that the reason we cannot find the

ABOVE *The planet Neptune, as photographed in 1989 by Voyager 2.*

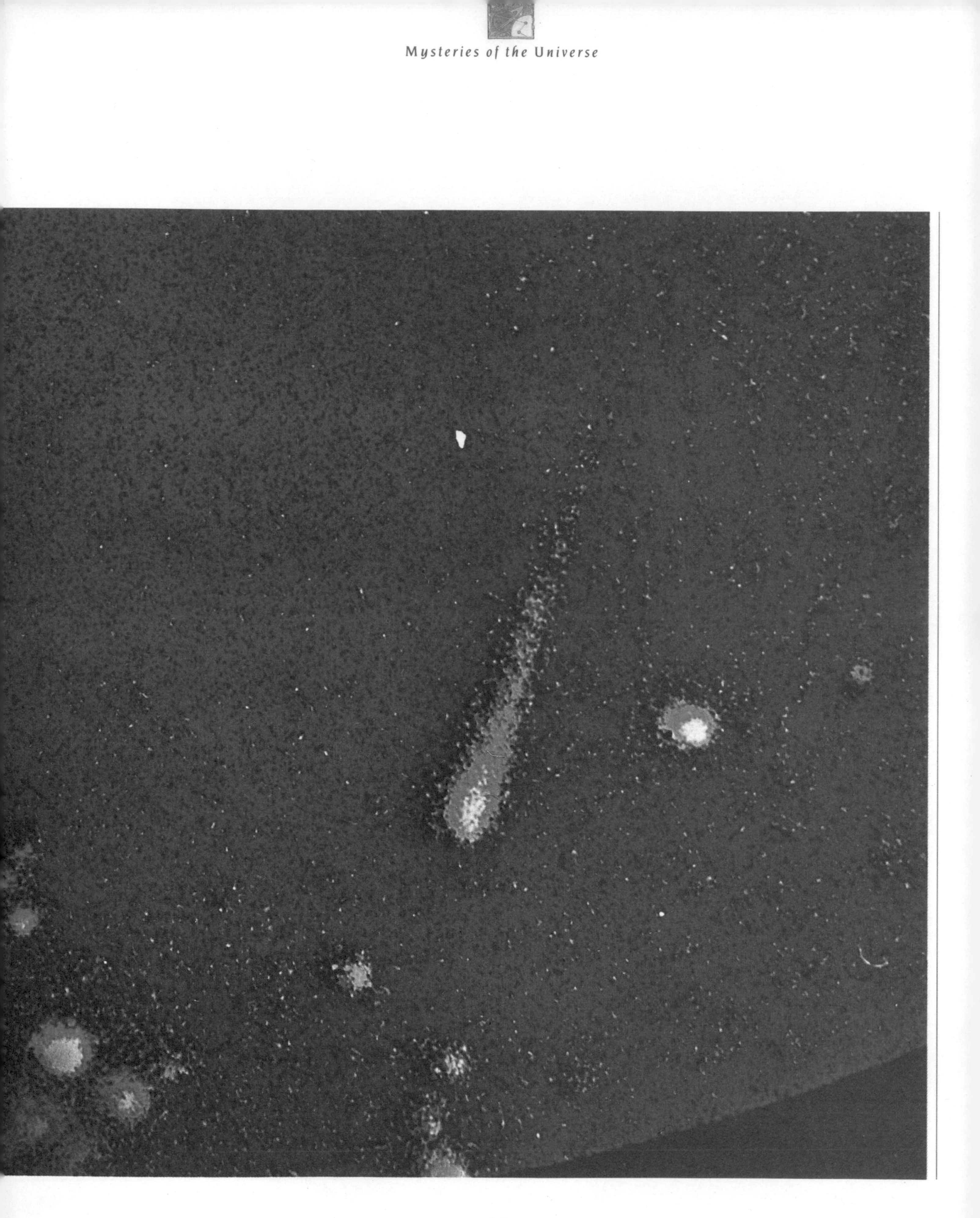

LEFT *The comet Kohoutek photographed in 1973 by Skylab 4.*
ABOVE *Comet Ikeya-Seki photographed by the US Naval Observatory in 1970.*

hypothetical tenth planet is that there is no such planet at all; rather there is, much further out, a black hole. Naturally such an entity would be hard to find, but its gravitational effect would be noticeable.

Our Sun is in a minority among the stars of the Universe in that it seems to be solitary. Most stars are members of double systems, where two stars orbit each other, and systems of three, four, five and even six stars are not uncommon; for example, the star nearest to ours, Proxima Centauri, is the third member of a system whose other two components, orbiting closely together, are jointly called α Centauri. So it would not be surprising if our Sun were in partnership with another star which had degenerated to become a black hole.

There is one difficulty with this. As we have seen, when stars collapse to form black holes an inevitable part of the process is a supernova. The radiation from this explosion would have sterilized all the planets of the Solar System while at the same time creating a huge, expanding shell of gases. However, such a consideration need not obviate the theory. The large stars that become supernovae are very short-lived by comparison with humbler stars like the Sun. The hard radiation from a supernova would be irrelevant to life if the explosion happened before life on Earth had begun to form – and might even have kick-started the process. Likewise, if the explosion occurred early enough in the Solar System's history, the shell of gases could long since have dissipated. A variant of the suggestion is that the Sun has a pulsar as a companion. All of the above considerations apply equally to this situation. One item of evidence in favour of these ideas is the behaviour of comets. It is now generally accepted that, about a lightyear from the Sun, far beyond the orbit of Pluto, there is a belt of at least 10 million comets, collectively known as the Oort Cloud, after the great Dutch astronomer Jan Oort. If the Solar System existed in total isolation, those comets would continue to orbit in perfectly stable fashion. However, the Solar System does not exist in isolation: the gravitational effects of nearby stars are, it is thought, sufficient to deflect some of the comets inwards to swing once – or more often – through the inner Solar System. How much more would a black hole, occasionally passing through or on the outskirts of the Oort Cloud, affect the comets?

If the arrivals of comets in the inner Solar System were totally haphazard we would have little reason to believe such ideas. However, the geological record of past ice ages shows that there is an uncanny regularity in their frequency. they occur approximately every 150 million years. One theory of the origin of ice ages is that they occur when large masses (for example, comets) crash down onto the Earth, throwing up vast amounts of detritus into the stratosphere which block off the heat from the Sun. This periodicity of the ice ages suggests that, once every 150 million years or so, the Earth is particularly vulnerable to cometary bombardment – in other words, that an unusually large number of comets enter the inner Solar System every 150 million years or so. One explanation for this regularity is that, about every 150 million years, a compact companion of the Sun (such as a pulsar or black hole), travelling in a very elliptical orbit, comes close enough to disrupt the comets of the Oort Cloud. What attracts many scientists to this hypothesis is that those perturbations of the orbits of Neptune and Pluto have yet to be explained satisfactorily in any other way.

Why Does the Sun Shine?

Every undergraduate astronomy student can tell you why the Sun shines: a series of nuclear fusion reactions, whose end result is the conversion of hydrogen to helium, happen on a vast scale, and release prodigious amounts of energy in the form of heat, light, X-rays and so on. A part of this reaction should be the release of neutrinos.

Neutrinos are hard to detect: they interact so little with matter that they can probably float through entire galaxies without being affected; they exist but have no mass nor any other physical property, which is like saying that they simultaneously exist and do not exist. Nevertheless, there are various ways by which scientists can detect their presence. The most effective is the use of a very large volume – 450,000 litres (100,000 gallons) – of carbon tetrachloride, better known as a cleaning fluid. In theory at least some neutrinos should react with the chlorine atoms in this mixture as they attempt to pass through it.

The trouble is that they seem not to. If the theory about the way that the Sun shines is correct, the Sun should produce about 180 billion billion billion billion neutrinos each second. Obviously only a small portion of these neutrinos will come in the Earth's direction, but still we ought to be in the path of about 80 billion billion billion neutrinos per second. Clearly, because of the elusive nature of neutrinos we cannot expect to capture all of them. But the results of the best 'neutrino-catching' experiment so far carried out are perhaps a little worse than the expectations of the most depressed pessimist: in 1965 a team of scientists recorded a grand total of seven neutrinos in nine months!

No one is certain why this should be. One possibility is that the Sun is currently going through a 'quiescent' phase: the nuclear reactions at its core are continuing just sufficiently to keep our star shining, but no more than that; in due course the Sun will get back to 'business as usual'. This idea is not very palatable: why should the Sun be anomalous just at the time that we start to search for neutrinos? Alternatively, perhaps neutrinos are much more elusive than we think, so that they evade with ease the traps we set them. A much more likely thesis is that the theory is wrong – either our ideas of the way in which stars function are wildly misplaced or our understanding of the process of nuclear fusion is flawed.

FAR LEFT *This photograph of the comet Kohoutek was taken with a 35mm camera in January 1974 by the lunar and planetary laboratory photographic team at the Catalina Observatory (University of Arizona).* **ABOVE** *Because of scattering in the atmosphere, the Sun's image appears reddened.*

BIBLIOGRAPHY

All of the books in this list are thought-provoking. However, their inclusion here does not mean that the various ideas they propose are necessarily valid. So, although these books are certainly worth reading, you would be well advised to treat them all with a fair degree of scepticism.

ALEKSANDER, IGOR, AND BURNETT, PIERS: *Reinventing Man*, London, Kogan Page, 1983.

ASHE, GEOFFREY: *The Ancient Wisdom*, London, Macmillan, 1977.

ASHE, GEOFFREY: *King Arthur's Avalon*, London, Collins, 1957.

BAXTER, JOHN, AND ATKINS, THOMAS: *The Fire Came By*, London, Macdonald & Jane's, 1976.

BEGG, PAUL: *Into Thin Air*, Newton Abbot, David & Charles, 1979.

BERLITZ, CHARLES: *Mysteries From Forgotten Worlds*, London, Souvenir, 1972.

BERLITZ, CHARLES: *The Mystery of Atlantis*, London, Souvenir, 1976.

BERNSTEIN, MOREY: *The Search for Bridey Murphy*, London, Hutchinson, 1956.

BOYCE, CHRIS: *Extraterrestrial Encounter*, Newton Abbot, David & Charles, 1979.

BRACEWELL, RONALD N: *The Galactic Club*, London, Heinemann, 1978.

BROOKESMITH, PETER (ED.): *The Alien World*, London, Orbis, 1984.

BUCK, ALICE E, AND PALMER, F CLAUDE: *The Clothes of God*, London, Peter Owen, 1956.

CALDWELL, TAYLOR, WITH STEARN, JESS: *The Romance of Atlantis*, London, Severn House, 1977.

CAPRA, FRITJOF: *The Tao of Physics*, London, Wildwood, 1975.

CATHIE, BRUCE: *The Pulse of the Universe: Harmonic 288*, London, Sphere, 1981.

CAVENDISH, RICHARD: A *History of Magic*, London, Weidenfeld & Nicholson, 1977.

CAVENDISH, RICHARD: *Unsolved Mysteries of the Universe*, London, Treasure Press, 1987.

CAVENDISH, RICHARD (ED.): *Encyclopedia of the Unexplained*, London, Routledge & Kegan Paul, 1974.

CHARROUX, ROBERT: *The Mysterious Unknown*, London, Spearman, 1972.

COCHRANE, HUGH H: *Gateway to Oblivion*, London Star, 1981.

COSTELLO, PETER: *The Magic Zoo*, London, Sphere, 1979.

CRAMER, MARC: *The Devil Within*, London, W. H. Allen, 1979.

CRICK, FRANCIS: *Life Itself*, London, Macdonald, 1982.

DAVIES, PAUL: *The Edge of Infinity*, London, Dent, 1981.

DAVIES, PAUL: *Other Worlds*, London, Dent, 1980.

DAVIES, PAUL: *Superforce*, London, Heinemann, 1984.

DAWKINS, RICHARD: *The Selfish Gene*, Oxford, OUP, 1976.

DIXON, BERNARD: *Beyond the Magic Bullet*, London, Allen & Unwin, 1978.

DIXON, BERNARD: *What is Science For?*, London, Collins, 1973.

DUNNE, J W: *An Experiment with Time* (5th edn.), London, Faber, 1939.

DYSON, FREEMAN: *Disturbing the Universe*, London, Harper & Row, 1979.

EDELSON, EDWARD: *Who Goes There?*, London, New English Library, 1980.

ELKINGTON, JOHN: *The Gene Factory*, London, Century, 1985.

EVANS, CHRISTOPHER: *Cults of Unreason*, London, Harrap, 1973.

EYSENCK, HANS J AND SARGET, CARL: *Explaining the Unexplained*, London, Weidenfeld & Nicholson, 1982.

FORT, CHARLES: *The Book of the Damned*, London, Abacus, 1973.

FOSTER, DAVID: *The Intelligent Universe*: London, Abelard-Schuman, 1975.

FRUDE, NEIL: *The Robot Heritage*, London, Century, 1984.

GIBSON, WALTER B, AND GIBSON, LITZKA R: *The Encyclopaedia of Prophecy*, London, Granada, 1977.

GLEICK, JAMES: *Chaos*, London, Heinemann, 1988.

GOLDSMITH, DONALD, AND OWEN, TOBIAS: *The Search for Life in the Universe*, Menlo Park (Cal), Benjamin/Cummings, 1980.

GOOCH, STAN: *The Paranormal*, London, Wildwood, 1978.

GOOCH, STAN: *Cities of Dreams*, London, Rider, 1989.

GOSS, MICHAEL: *The Evidence for Phantom Hitch-hikers*, Wellingborough, Aquarian Press, 1984.

GOULD, STEPHEN JAY: *The Mismeasure of Man*, New York, Norton, 1981.

GRANT, DOUGLAS: *The Cock Lane Ghost*, London, Macmillan, 1965.

GRANT, JOAN: *Winged Pharaoh*, London, Arthur Barker, 1937 (novel).

GRANT, JOHN: *A Directory of Discarded Ideas*, Sevenoaks, Ashgrove Press, 1981.

GRANT, JOHN: *Dreamers*, Bath, Ashgrove Press, 1984.

GRANT, JOHN: 'The Flight of Reason', *Common Ground*, November 1981.

GRANT, JOHN: 'Not Such a Tippe-top Idea', *Common Ground*, May 1982.

GRANT, JOHN: *Sex Secrets of Ancient Atlantis*, London, Grafton, 1985.

GRANT, JOHN: 'Things That Go Crank in the Night', *Common Ground*, February 1982.

GRANT, JOHN (ED.): *The Book of Time* (Consultant Editor Colin Wilson), Newton Abbot, Westbridge, 1980.

GREENE, GRAHAM: *A Sort of Life*, London, Bodley Head, 1971.

GRIBBIN, JOHN: *Timewarps*, London, Dent, 1979.

GRIBBIN, JOHN: *In Search of Schrödinger's Cat*, London, Wildwood, 1984.

GURNEY, EDMUND, MYERS, FREDERIC W H, AND PODMORE, FRANK: *Phantasms of the Living*, London, Society for Psychical Research and Trübner, 1886.

HARRINGTON, ALAN: *The Immortalist*, St Albans, Granada, 1973.

HARRISON, MICHAEL: *Vanishings*, London, New English Library, 1981.

HERBERT, NICK: *Quantum Reality*, London, Rider, 1985.

HEUVELMANS, BERNARD: *In the Wake of the Sea-Serpents*, London, Rupert Hart-Davis, 1986 (trans.).

HEUVELMANS, BERNARD: *On the Track of Unknown Animals*, London, Paladin, 1970 (abridged trans.).

HOYLE, FRED, AND WICKRAMASINGHE, NC: *Evolution from Space*, London, Dent, 1981.

HOYLE, FRED, AND WICKRAMASINGHE, NC: *Lifecloud*, London, Dent, 1978.

HUGHES, DAVID: *The Star of Bethlehem Mystery*, London, Dent, 1979.

JASTROW, ROBERT: *Until the Sun Dies*, New York, Norton, 1977.

JOHN, BRIAN (ED.): *The Winters of the World*, Newton Abbot, David & Charles, 1979.

JONAS, DORIS AND JONAS, DAVID: *Other Senses, Other Worlds*, London, Cassell, 1976.

JONES, ROGER: *Physics as Metaphor*, London, Wildwood, 1983.

KOESTLER, ARTHUR: *The Roots of Coincidence*, London, Hutchinson, 1972.

KOLOSIMO, PETER: *Timeless Earth*, London, Sphere, 1974 (trans.).

KRUPP, E C (ED.): *In Search of Ancient Astronomies*, London, Chatto & Windus, 1980.

LANDSBURG, ALAN: *In Search of Myths and Monsters*, London, Corgi, 1977.

LAWTON, AT: *A Window in the Sky*, Newton Abbot, David & Charles, 1979.

LEAKEY, RICHARD E, AND LEWIN, ROGER: *Origins*, London, Macdonald & Jane's, 1977.

LEONARD, GEORGE H: *Someone Else is on Our Moon*, London, W. H. Allen, 1977.

LESLIE, DESMOND, AND ADAMSKI, GEORGE: *Flying Saucers Have Landed*, London, Futura, 1977.

LOOSLEY, WILLIAM ROBERT: *An Account of a Meeting with Denizens of Another World, 1871*, 'edited' by David Langford, Newton Abbot, David & Charles, 1979.

LUNAN, DUNCAN: *Man and the Planets*, Bath, Ashgrove, 1983.

MCCLURE, KEVIN: *The Evidence for Visions of the Virgin Mary*, Aquarian Press, Wellingborough, 1983.

MCCONNELL, BRIAN, AND BENCE, DOUGLAS: *The Nilsen File*, London, Futura, 1983.

MACKAL, ROY P: *The Monsters of Loch Ness*, London, Futura, 1976.

MAPLE, ERIC: *The Realm of Ghosts*, London, Hale, 1964.

MASTERS, ANTHONY: *The Natural History of the Vampire*, London, Granada, 1974.

MAVOR, JAMES W: *Voyage to Atlantis*, London, Souvenir, 1969.

MENZEL, DONALD H, AND TAVES, ERNEST H: *The UFO Enigma*, Garden City (NJ), Doubleday, 1977.

MICHELL, JOHN, AND RICKARD, ROBERT J M: *Phenomena*, London, Thames & Hudson, 1977.

MOORE, PATRICK: *Can You Speak Venusian?*, Newton Abbot, David & Charles, 1972.

MORGAN, CHRIS: *Future Man*, Newton Abbot, David & Charles, 1980.

MORGAN, CHRIS, AND LANGFORD, DAVID: *Facts and Fallacies*, Exeter, Webb & Bower, 1981.

NAPIER, JOHN: *Bigfoot*, London, Cape, 1972.

NARLIKAR, JAYANT V: *Violent Phenomena in the Universe*, Oxford, OUP, 1982.

NASH, JAY ROBERT: *Compendium of World Crime*, London, Harrap, 1983 (originally published in the United States as *Almanac of World Crime*, 1981).

NICOLSON, IAIN: *Gravity, Black Holes and the Universe*, Newton Abbot, David & Charles, 1981.

NICOLSON, IAIN: *The Road to the Stars*, Newton Abbot, Westbridge, 1978.

NOORBERGEN, RENE: *Secrets of the Lost Races*, London, New English Library, 1978.

PANATI, CHARLES: *Supersenses*, London, Cape, 1975.

PEDLER, KIT: *Mind Over Matter*, London, Eyre Methuen, 1981.

PERCY, WALKER: *Lost in the Cosmos*, London, Arena, 1984.

PERMUTT, CYRIL: *Beyond the Spectrum*, Cambridge, Patrick Stephens, 1983.

PLAYFAIR, GUY LYON: *The Indefinite Boundary*, London, Souvenir, 1976.

PLAYFAIR, GUY LYON: *The Unknown Power*, London, Granada, 1977 (originally published as *The Flying Cow*).

RANDLES, JENNY: *The Pennine UFO Mystery*, London, Grafton, 1983.

RANDLES, JENNY, AND WHETNALL, PAUL: *Alien Contact*, London, Coronet, 1983.

RENFREW, COLIN: *Before Civilization*, London, Cape, 1973.

ROWAN-ROBINSON, MICHAEL: *Cosmic Landscape*, Oxford, OUP, 1979.

SACHS, MARGARET: *The UFO Encyclopedia*, London, Corgi, 1981.

SAGAN, CARL: *Broca's Brain*, London, Hodder & Stoughton, 1979.

SAGAN, CARL: *The Dragons of Eden*, New York, Random, 1977.

SAGAN, CARL, AND DRUYAN, ANN: *Comet*, London, Michael Joseph, 1985.

SASSOON, GEORGE, AND DALE, RODNEY: *The Manna Machine*, London, Sidgwick & Jackson, 1978.

SLADEK, JOHN: *The New Apocrypha*, London, Hart-Davis MacGibbon, 1974.

SMITH, ADAM: *Powers of Mind*, London, W. H. Allen, 1976.

STONELEY, JACK, AND LAWTON, A T: *CETI*, London, Star 1976.

STONELEY, JACK AND LAWTON AT: *Is Anyone Out There?*, London, Star, 1975.

STONELEY, JACK, AND LAWTON, AT: *Tunguska: Cauldron of Hell*, London, Star, 1977.

STORY, RONALD: *Guardians of the Universe*, London, New English Library, 1980.

STORY, RONALD: *The Space-Gods Revealed*, London, New English Library, 1978.

SULLIVAN, WALTER: *We Are Not Alone*, London, Hodder, 1965.

VAUGHAN, ALAN: *Patterns of Prophecy*, London, Turnstone, 1974.

VON DÄNIKEN, ERICH: *Chariots of the Gods?*, London, Souvenir, 1969 (trans.).

WARING, PHILIPPA: *A Dictionary of Omens and Superstitions*, London, Souvenir, 1978.

WARLOW, PETER: *The Reversing Earth*, London, Dent, 1982.

WARSHOFSKY, FRED: *Doomsday*, London, Sphere, 1979.

WATSON, LYALL: *Lifetide*, London, Hodder & Stoughton, 1979.

WATSON, LYALL: *Supernature*, London, Hodder & Stoughton, 1973.

WATSON, PETER: *Twins*, London, Hutchinson, 1981.

WEBB, JAMES: *The Occult Establishment*, Glasgow, Richard Drew, 1981.

WEINBERG, STEVEN: *The First Three Minutes*, London, Deutsch, 1977.

WELLARD, JAMES: *The Search for Lost Worlds*, London, Pan, 1975.

WHITE, BURTON L: *The First Three Years of Life*, London, WH Allen, 1978.

WHITROW, G J: *The Nature of Time*, Harmondsworth, Penguin, 1975.

WILSON, COLIN: *Starseekers*, Garden City, Doubleday, 1980.

WILSON, COLIN, AND GRANT, JOHN (EDS.): *The Book of Time*, Newton Abbot, Westbridge, 1980.

WILSON, COLIN: *A Criminal History of Mankind*, London, Granada, 1984.

WILSON, COLIN: *Mysteries*, London, Hodder & Stoughton, 1978.

WILSON, COLIN: *Poltergeist!*, London, New English Library, 1981.

WILSON, COLIN, AND GRANT, JOHN (EDS.): *The Directory of Possibilities*: Exeter, Webb & Bower, 1981.

WRIGHT, PETER, AND GREENGRASS, PAUL: *Spycatcher*, New York, Viking, 1987.

INDEX

Page numbers in **bold** indicate illustrations or their captions.

C

D

J

L

M

N

P

Picture Credits

Janet & Colin Bord: 31, 187; *The British Museum*, 46, 160*l*; CERN; 180, 201; *Jean-Loup Charmet*: 30, 69, 74, 75, 76, 77*l*, 78*r*, 81, 118*b*, 119*r*, 120*b*; *John H. Cutten*: 11, 14, 15, 16, 20, 24, 41*tr* & *b*, 52, 53, 56*t*, 95, 174*tr*, 175; C. M. *Dixon*: 127, 130, 148, 149, 160*r*, 161, 162, 163, 164–5, 166; *Dover Publications*: 115*r*; *The Dracula Society*: 77*r*; *Liz Eddison*: 144–5, 182, 183, 192, 193; ET *Archive*: 13, 28, 34, 35, 40, 41*tl*, 51, 57, 72, 73; *Mary Evans Picture Library*: 10*t*, 12, 25, 33, 37, 42, 44, 47, 48, 50, 56*b*, 59, 60*b*, 97, 101, 102, 103*b*, 105, 107*tl* & *b*, 108, 109, 114, 116, 117, 118*t*, 121, 125, 128, 131, 136, 151, 159, 168, 172*r*, 176–7, 185, 186, 188, 189, 190, 191, 192; *Mary Evans Picture Library/Arne Thomassen*: 112*bl*; *Mary Evans Picture Library/Playfair*: 26–7; *Mary Evans Picture Library/Society for Psychical Research*: 12*b*, 32; *Fortean Picture Library*: 7, 38, 39, 40*bl*, 49, 60*t*, 64, 65, 66, 67, 68, 70, 71, 79, 80, 82, 83, 84, 85, 86, 87, 88, 89, 90, 91, 92, 93, 94, 94–5 (*background*), 96, 98, 100*t*, 103*t*, 106*l*, 107*tr*, 110, 112*tr*, 113, 120*t* & *m*, 146, 150; GSF *Picture Library*: 129, 132, 138, 139, 156–7, 169, 172*l*, 177 (*inset*), 215; *Harper Bros*: 115*l*; *Lorraine Harrison*: 122–3, 134–5, 137, 167, 170–1, 184–5, 196–7; *The Hulton Picture Library*: 194, 195, 198, 209; IBM: 124, 133; *Nick Law*; 61; *The Mansell Collection*: 17, 18, 19, 21, 29, 42, 45, 58, 78*l*; *Ned Middleton*: 179; NASA: 143, 144*t*, 152, 153, 154, 155, 203*b*, 204, 207, 208, 210 211, 212, 213, 214; *Natural History Museum*: 1451*r*; *Nuffield Radio Astronomy Laboratories*: 205; *Philosophical Research Institute Inc.*, LA: 23; *Jenny Randles*: 100*b*, 101*b*, 104; *Jim Robins*: 145*b*; *Ann Ronan Picture Library*: 173, 174*l*, 178–9, 199, 200; *The Rover Group*: 181; *Royal Observatory, Edinburgh*: 158, 203*t*; *Robert Temple*: 126.